DEEP
SKY
OBJECTS

A Photographic Guide
for the Amateur

Jack Newton

Dedication

I dedicate this book to my wife, Janet, who spent many lonely nights while this book was being prepared.

Acknowledgements

I would also like to acknowledge the following people: Bob Bennie, Moody Kalbfleisch, Hines Lorenz, Frank Shinn, and my publisher, who is a genius at creating practical star charts. Special thanks to the Royal Astronomical Society of Canada and their *Observer's Handbook* by John Percy and the Astronomical League for *Observe, An Observing Program for use with Small Instruments* by Edward Holyoke.

Cataloguing in Publication Information

Newton, Jack, 1942-
  Deep sky objects

ISBN 0-88904-081-8

1. Astronomy - Observers' manuals. I. Title.

QB64.N49   522   C77-001384-8

Published by

GALL Publications
1293 Gerrard Street East, Toronto, Canada, M4L 1Y8
Text © 1977 by GALL Publications
Photographs © 1977 by Jack Newton

Computer typesetting by *alphatext*.

Printed in Canada

Contents

3

Contents (Continued)

Introduction

This guide was prepared to help amateur astronomers locate and identify the Messier objects and some of the more interesting NGC numbers.

Included are full-page photographs of most of the interesting sights in the night sky. The pictures were all taken at the prime focus of my 12.5-inch Newtonian telescope and were printed to about the same scale. Each photograph covers approximately one degree from top to bottom, or twice the height of the full moon, see page 11. You will be able to see at a glance the apparent size and brightness of each object. This makes it easy to choose the most suitable targets for your particular telescope.

Beside most photographs there are detailed finder charts which show the location in relation to well-known stars and constellation asterisms. The main charts at the end of the book will help you orient yourself to the sky at any time of night.

You will notice the month shown on all charts. The date is when that particular meridian is directly south at midnight Daylight time or 11 p.m. Standard time. (The meridians appear as vertical lines on all charts. Two months named indicates the beginning of one and the end of the other.)

For observing Deep Sky Objects, it is more advantageous to look at them when they are as close to your meridian as possible. Your local meridian extends from Polaris, the North Star, directly overhead and down to a point directly south on the horizon.

As the night progresses a new meridian is directly south every hour. This in effect allows you to look into the future. That is, if you stay up past midnight, you will be able to preview the sky for next month. If you stay up into the morning, you will be able to see two, three or, in the case of winter, even four months into the future. Of course by looking toward the east you will be able to preview the objects and by looking west you will be able to review what you saw the previous month.

Throughout the book I have referred to small, medium and large telescopes. A small telescope refers to a maximum aperture of 4 inches. The medium scope is generally between 6 and 10 inches and a large amateur telescope is anything greater.

Magnification has been mentioned as low, medium and high. Low means under 50x, high is over 200x and medium is in between.

Deep Sky Objects is a term used to describe astronomical phenomena beyond our solar system; some are even beyond our galaxy.

Solar System describes our Sun and its family of planets, including Earth, our home. The Sun, a medium-sized star, is located in one of the spiral arms of the Milky Way Galaxy half way from the edge of the galaxy to the central nucleus.

Milky Way Galaxy contains about 1500 million stars, is about 100,000 light years across and we are located around 26,000 light years from its centre.

Open star clusters are loose groups of stars located in our own galaxy. They may contain as few as four bright stars such as the Trapezium in Orion, page 54, or many thousands as in the double cluster in Perseus, page 92. Many open clusters are easily seen with the naked eye. The Pleiades or Seven Sisters, page 59, and Praesepe or the Beehive, page 57, are examples. Most of the rest can be seen in binoculars.

External galaxies are within the reach of any amateur telescope. Within our immediate area we have the Local Group of galaxies which consists of about thirty components. The closest is known as the LMC or the Large Magellanic Cloud, about 160,000 light years away. The largest on pages 40 and 41, is the Great Andromeda Galaxy which recently has been estimated to be over 2 million light years away. The Sombrero galaxy, page 123, is over 35 million light years away, yet it can be seen in a small telescope. On the border between the Coma and the Virgo cluster of galaxies is a concentration of over 10,000 separate galaxies, some 40 million light years away. A medium telescope will show as many as half a dozen galaxies in the same low-power field. See page 103.

Elliptical galaxies are thought to be young galaxies that have either not formed spiral arms or have lost them through collision with other galaxies.

Supernova remnants are the result of a stellar explosion many years ago. A good example is the Crab on page 13.

Diffuse nebulae are large clouds of gas and dust within our galaxy. The Great Orion Nebula, page 55 and the front cover, is an enormous cloud of excited hydrogen activated by hot young stars. In photographs it appears bright red, yet visually to the unaided eye it appears a pale green. Many of the brighter nebulae are shown throughout this book.

Dark nebulae are much more difficult to observe. Essentially they are clouds of dust and gas that obscure the light from distant stars and nebulae. The Horsehead, page 53 and back cover, is one of the most striking examples. Dark dust lanes can also be observed in many of the external galaxies such as NGC 4565 on page 134.

Planetary nebulae are shells of expanding gas illuminated by a central star. They look like a distant planet, thus their name. This round shape can appear as a ring, page 73, or a dumbbell, page 37.

Globular clusters are associated with our galaxy and are given that name because of their round shapes. They contain from 10 thousand to over a million stars and are most richly distributed above and below the galactic plane. The Great Cluster in Hercules, page 27, can just barely be made out with the naked eye on a dark night. With binoculars it looks like a large fuzzy spot, but it is absolutely fantastic in anything larger. There are 28 globular clusters in the Messier Catalogue, all visible with a 2-inch telescope.

Jack Newton and his 12.5 inch telescope

Newton Observatory at the Innisfil Complex

Please note: The pictures in this book appear much brighter than you will probably observe in your small telescope! Photographic film stores the light and the human eye does not. Your sky conditions and experience will vary greatly as does the optical quality of the instrument you use. All three factors will affect what you see. By studying the photographs before observing, you will find that they will guide you in identification of the fainter objects.

Very few professional or amateur astronomers can make claim to having seen all of the Messier objects, even after a lifetime of observation.

The **Observing Programme** starting on page 137 will help you to identify all bright stars in each constellation and help you find the objects that are best placed for the times shown.

To help you understand how the sky changes, imagine that you are on a great spaceship called Earth. Your home is whirling around once every 24 hours and you journey about the star we call the Sun once every year at more than 60,000 miles per hour.

Astrophotography, a hobby within a hobby, allows you to make a record of your astronomical observations. It need not be complicated as almost any adjustable camera will afford remarkable results when turned toward the sky. The pictures of the Pleiades, page 58, and the Beehive, page 56, were both taken with a 200 mm, f4.5 telephoto lens. Note the famous Horsehead nebula on page 52. It was captured after only 20 minutes of exposure using the same system piggy-backed on a small hand-guided telescope.

The balance of the **photographs** were taken at the prime focus of my 12.5-inch, f4.6 Newtonian telescope with a focal length of 58 inches. The star clusters were exposed for about 13 minutes and the other objects for about 20. Kodak Tri-X and 103AF spectroscopic films were used and developed for 5 minutes in D19. The paper was Ilford number 5, high contrast. Quite often as much time was taken in the darkroom developing and printing the pictures as was originally spent outside at the telescope.

The **telescope** is housed in a small home-made observatory about 40 miles north of Toronto, a city of nearly 3 million people. The telescope is the basement workshop variety and weighs over 500 pounds. Its barrel, housing the optics, is made of 'Sona tube' usually used to form concrete pillars. The mount was constructed from junkyard scrap with a commercially purchased clock drive. A very heavy telescope is best suited for astrophotography as the mass provides greater stability in wind and permits the addition of heavy accessories, such as a guide scope and camera.

The **guide telescope** was a 3-inch Tasco, 1200 mm in focal length. A 12 mm eyepiece with an illuminated crosshair was used in conjunction with a 3x Barlow lens providing 300x magnification. A simple formula for guiding is 5x for every inch of focal length used. For example: A telescope with a focal length of 1200 mm or about 50 inches, should have 5 x 50 or 250x magnification for easy guiding.

The **camera** used on my telescope was a 35 mm single lens reflex with a self-timer triggered with a cable release allowing the mirror to release 10 seconds prior to the shutter opening. Thus all vibration stops before the film is exposed. With a lot of perseverance, good luck and a firm heel on Murphy's forehead, fine astrophotography can be accomplished.

(Murphy's Law states: Whatever can go wrong . . . will!)

For further reading, we recommend:

Astronomy Magazine, 411 East Mason Street, Milwaukee, WI, 53202

Sky & Telescope, 49 Bay State Road, Cambridge, MA, 02138

Skalnate Pleso Atlas of the Heavens, c/o Sky & Telescope

Norton Star Atlas, c/o Sky & Telescope

Galaxies, Shapely, Harvard University Press, Cambridge, MA 02138

The Milky Way, Bok and Bok, Harvard University Press

Observer's Handbook, R.A.S.C., 124 Merton St, Toronto, Canada

When You Can Avoid the Moon

During **March and April** the FULL Moon rises in the east just as the sun sets. Each day after the Calendar Full Moon it will rise about 45 minutes later.

From **May to August** it will rise south of the eastern point after sunset and about 30 minutes later on the following nights.

In **September and October** it rises again in the east as the sun sets and about 45 minutes later each night after the Full Moon.

From **November to February** it will rise north of the easterly point just before sunset and about one hour later each night.

One week after FULL Moon we have the LAST Quarter which generally rises around midnight.

Deep Sky Objects are best viewed in the evening from the LAST Quarter until a couple of days before FIRST Quarter.

At **FIRST Quarter** the moon will not set until Midnight or later.

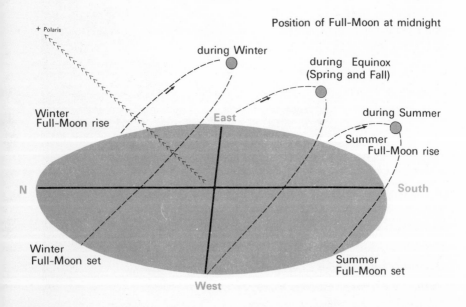

Diagram showing apparent path of Full Moon in Summer, Winter and the Equinoxes

Relative size of the Moon taken at the prime focus of the 12.5 inch telescope

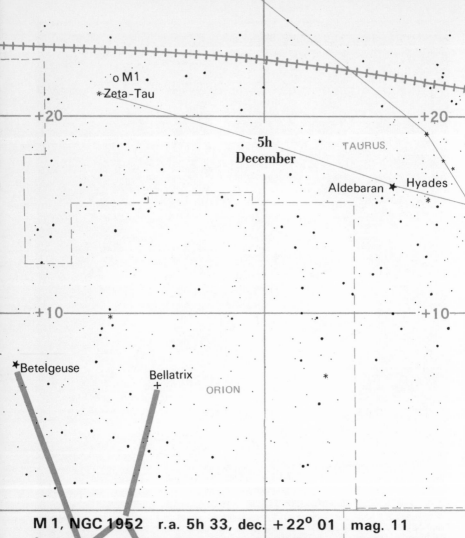

o M1
*Zeta-Tau

+20   +20

5h
December   TAURUS.

Aldebaran ★   Hyades

+10   +10

★Betelgeuse

Bellatrix
+

ORION

M 1, NGC 1952   r.a. 5h 33, dec. +22° 01   mag. 11

Supernova remnant in Taurus about 4000 light years away. Chinese astronomers observed a supernova in Taurus during the year 1054. We believe that the diffuse nebula now known as the **Crab** is a remnant of this explosion. The gas is still expanding at about 800 miles per second. The central star was one of the first photographed pulsar or neutron stars. It pulsates about 30 times per second and has contracted to about 200 miles in diameter. It is said that one tablespoon of its matter would weigh as much as five billion tons here on Earth. This tiny patch of light with low surface brightness is definitely a real challenge for the beginning observer. A large telescope is required to show the irregular shape. *Look just north of Zeta-Tau.* **(December)**

Crab Nebula M 1, NGC 1952

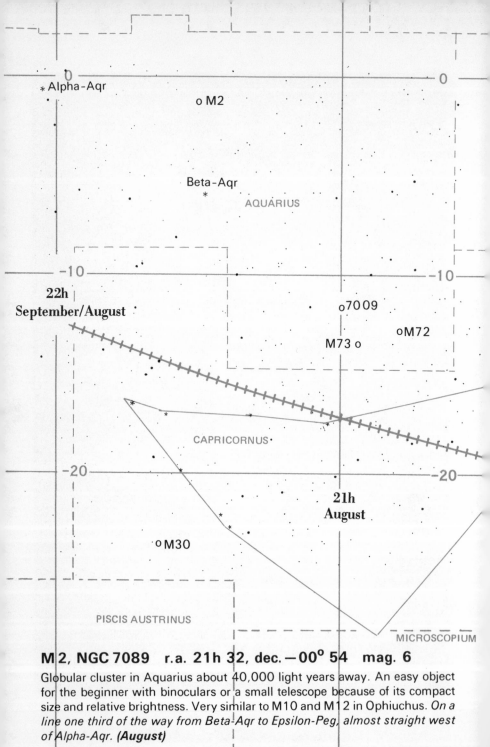

M2, NGC 7089   r.a. 21h 32, dec. −00° 54   mag. 6

Globular cluster in Aquarius about 40,000 light years away. An easy object for the beginner with binoculars or a small telescope because of its compact size and relative brightness. Very similar to M10 and M12 in Ophiuchus. *On a line one third of the way from Beta-Aqr to Epsilon-Peg, almost straight west of Alpha-Aqr. (August)*

Globular Cluster M 3, NGC 5272

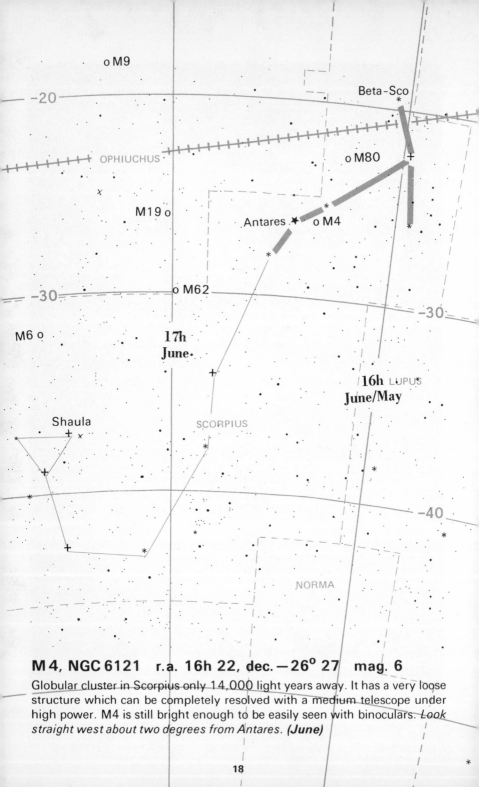

o M9

Beta-Sco

−20

OPHIUCHUS

o M80

x

M19 o

Antares ✶ o M4

−30

o M62

M6 o

17h
June

16h LUPUS
June/May

Shaula
x

SCORPIUS

−30

−40

NORMA

M 4, NGC 6121   r.a. 16h 22, dec. −26° 27   mag. 6
Globular cluster in Scorpius only 14,000 light years away. It has a very loose
structure which can be completely resolved with a medium telescope under
high power. M4 is still bright enough to be easily seen with binoculars. *Look
straight west about two degrees from Antares. (June)*

Globular Cluster M 4, NGC 6121

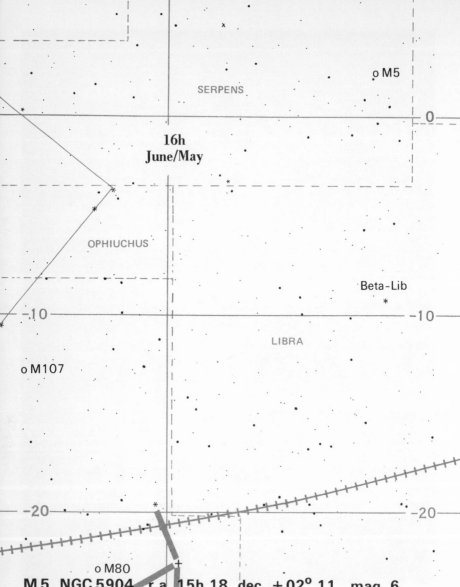

SERPENS

o M5

16h
June/May

0

OPHIUCHUS

Beta-Lib
*

-10

-10

LIBRA

o M107

-20

-20

o M80

+

M 5, NGC 5904 r.a. 15h 18, dec. +02° 11   mag. 6

Globular cluster in Serpens about 25,000 light years away. Thought to be about 22 billion years old, this is one of the oldest known clusters. Important for its many RR Lyra variable stars with periods of less than a day, the amateur can observe the two interesting 25.7 and 26.4 day W-Virginis Variables which change from 11th to 12th magnitude. Look for them on the southern side of the cluster. One is close and the other quite a distance from the ball of stars. *Straight north about ten degrees from Beta-Lib . (May)*

Globular Cluster M 5, NGC 5904

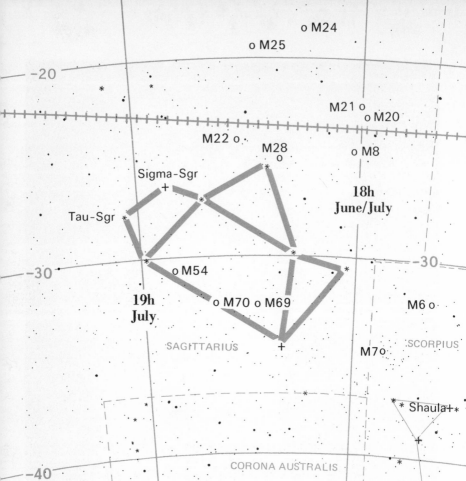

M 6, NGC 6405   r.a. 17h 39, dec. −32° 11   mag. 6

Open cluster in Scorpius about 1500 light years away. Easily resolved with a small telescope and medium power. *Straight north of the 'Tail' in Scorpius to a line west from the top of the spout of the 'Teapot' in Sagittarius. (June)*

M 7, NGC 6475   r.a. 17h 53, dec. −34° 48   mag. 5

Open cluster in Scorpius only 750 light years distant. Nearly twice as far away as the Pleiades and looks like a fuzzy spot to the naked eye on a dark night. Can be completely resolved with high power and a medium telescope. *Just south of M6. (June)*

M 8, NGC 6523   r.a. 18h 02, dec. −24° 23

Diffuse nebula in Sagittarius about 4500 light years away. The **Lagoon** is almost the size of the full moon and is as impressive in southern latitudes as M42 is in the north. The brightness is due to ultraviolet radiation from young hot stars. Look one degree north for M20, the Trifid. *Easy to find by looking for the steam from the 'Teapot' in Sagittarius. (July)*

Lagoon Nebula M 8, NGC 6523

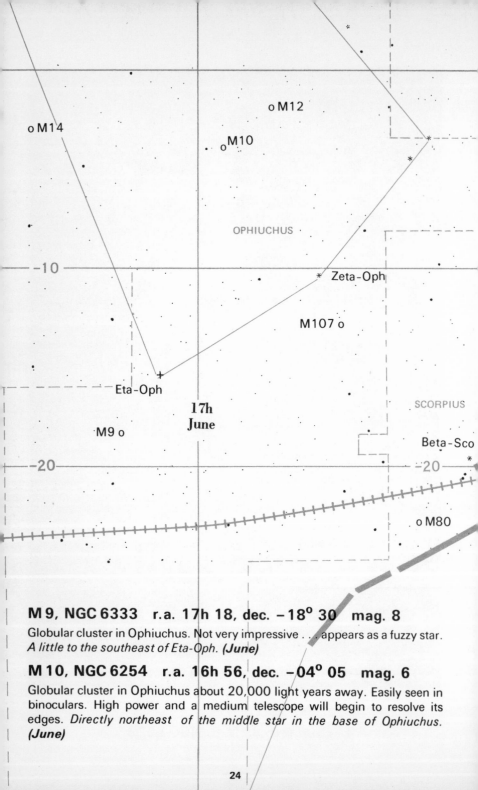

o M14

o M12

o M10

OPHIUCHUS

Zeta-Oph

M107 o

+
Eta-Oph

17h
June

M9 o

SCORPIUS

Beta-Sco

-20   -20

o M80

-10   -10

M 9, NGC 6333   r.a. 17h 18, dec. −18° 30   mag. 8

Globular cluster in Ophiuchus. Not very impressive . . . appears as a fuzzy star.
A little to the southeast of Eta-Oph. (June)

M 10, NGC 6254   r.a. 16h 56, dec. −04° 05   mag. 6

Globular cluster in Ophiuchus about 20,000 light years away. Easily seen in
binoculars. High power and a medium telescope will begin to resolve its
edges. *Directly northeast of the middle star in the base of Ophiuchus.
(June)*

Globular Cluster M 10, NGC 6254

M92 o

17h
June

+40   +40

* Eta-Her

o M13

HERCULES   16h
                                           June/May

* Zeta-Her   CORONA   BOREALIS

+30   +30

M 11, NGC 6705   r.a. 18h 50, dec. −06° 18   mag. 7

Open cluster in Scutum about 5000 light years distant. Somewhat fan-shaped it is known as the **Wild Duck Cluster** and often compared to a flock of geese in flight. Low power in a small telescope will resolve it. The stars are so tightly packed together that a larger scope will afford a much better view. *Just west of Lambda-Aql. See page 30 for finder chart. (July)*

M 12, NGC 6218   r.a. 16h 46, dec. −01° 55   mag. 7

Globular cluster in Ophiuchus about 25,000 light years away. A twin of M10 in practically every respect except that it is 5000 light years farther away. High power on a medium telescope will just begin to resolve the edges. See page 24 for finder chart. *A little to the northeast of M10. (June)*

M 13, NGC 6205   r.a. 16h 41, dec. +36° 30   mag. 6

Globular cluster in Hercules about 20,000 light years away. This **Great Cluster in Hercules** is considered to be the jewel box of the northern sky. It can be seen with the naked eye on a dark night and is believed to contain half a million stars. Use all the magnification you have for an absolutely fantastic view. A small telescope shows it as a fuzzy ball with a bright centre, a larger scope will start to resolve its nucleus. Note NGC 6207 centered near the top of the photograph. *Two-thirds of the way from Zeta-Her to Eta-Her.*

(June)

Great Cluster in Hercules M 13, NGC 6205

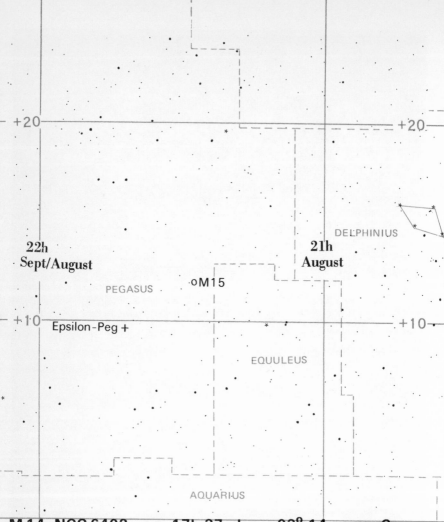

+20 +20

DELPHINIUS

22h
Sept/August

21h
August

PEGASUS ∘M15

+10 +10
Epsilon-Peg +

EQUULEUS

AQUARIUS

M 14, NGC 6402   r.a. 17h 37, dec. −03° 14   mag. 8

Globular cluster in Ophiuchus. Famous for the nova discovered in 1938 by Dr. Helen Hogg and her associate. Extremely compact, a medium telescope with high power will only begin to resolve the edges. *One third of the way from Beta-Oph to Eta-Oph and a little east. See page 24 for finder chart. (June)*

M 15, NGC 7078   r.a. 21h 29, dec. +12° 05   mag. 6

Globular cluster in Pegasus 35,000 light years away. Similar to both M10 and M12 in magnitude, yet nearly twice the distance! Fairly compact, the outer stars can be resolved under high power with a medium telescope. Easily picked off with binoculars. *Three degrees northwest of Epsilon-Peg. (August)*

Globular Cluster M 15, NGC 7078

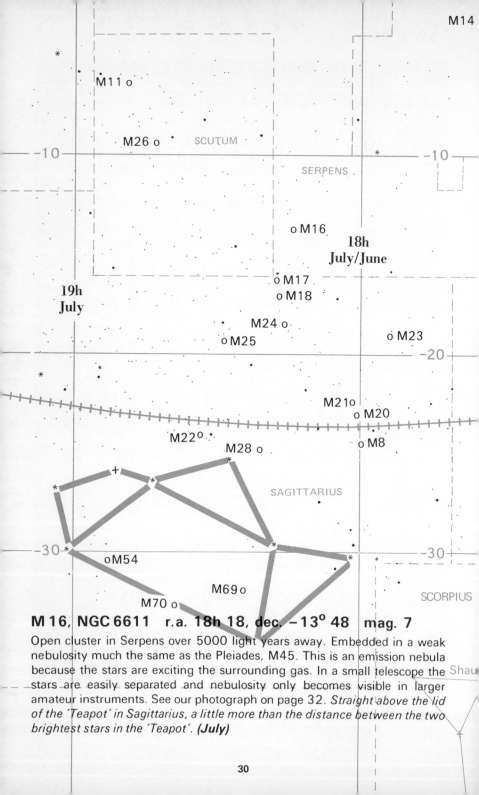

M11 o

M26 o   SCUTUM

−10 ———————————————————————————————— −10

SERPENS

o M16

18h
July/June

o M17
o M18

19h
July

M24 o
o M25

ó M23

−20

M21o
o M20

M22º

M28 o

o M8

SAGITTARIUS

−30 —   oM54   −30

M69 o

M70 o

M 16, NGC 6611   r.a. 18h 18, dec. −13° 48   mag. 7

SCORPIUS

Open cluster in Serpens over 5000 light years away. Embedded in a weak
nebulosity much the same as the Pleiades, M45. This is an emission nebula
because the stars are exciting the surrounding gas. In a small telescope the
stars are easily separated and nebulosity only becomes visible in larger
amateur instruments. See our photograph on page 32. *Straight above the lid
of the 'Teapot' in Sagittarius, a little more than the distance between the two
brightest stars in the 'Teapot'.* *(July)*

M 17, NGC 6618   r.a. 18h 20, dec. −16° 12   mag. 7

Diffuse nebula in Sagittarius about 3000 light years distant. Commonly called the **Omega** or **Horseshoe Nebula** because of its resemblance to the Greek letter. A binocular object. Visually it appears as a misty white, but when photographed on colour film, it has a reddish tint. See page 33 for photograph. *About 2 degrees south of M16. (July)*

M 18, NGC 6613   r.a. 18h 19, dec. −17° 09   mag. 7

Open cluster in Sagittarius. Hard to separate from the rich surroundings in the Milky Way. *One degree south of M17. (July)*

M 19, NGC 6273   r.a. 17h 01, dec. −26° 14   mag. 7

Globular cluster in Ophiuchus. Highly compact and embedded in the Milky Way. *(June)*

M 20, NGC 6514   r.a. 18h 01, dec. −23° 02

Diffuse nebula in Sagittarius 3500 light years away. The **Trifid** is remarkable for its distinct dust lanes visible in medium telescopes. See page 34 for the photograph. On colour film the lower half is a reddish emission nebula. The upper half is a bluish reflection nebula. *Just above M8. (July)*

M 21, NGC 6531   r.a. 18h 03, dec. −22° 30   mag. 7

Open cluster in Sagittarius. See page 34 in the upper left-hand corner of the picture. *(July)*

M 22, NGC 6656   r.a. 18h 35, dec. −23° 55   mag. 5

Globular cluster in Sagittarius about 10,000 light years away. Is a southern-sky rival for M13. A must for all telescopes. *(July)*

M 23, NGC 6494   r.a. 17h 56, dec. −19° 00   mag. 6

Open cluster in Sagittarius only 1500 light years away. All 200 members of this cluster are resolved with a medium scope. *(June)*

M 24, NGC 6603   r.a. 18h 17, dec. −18° 27   mag. 6

Open cluster in Sagittarius. Very difficult to see in these rich star fields. *(July)*

M 25, NGC 4725   r.a. 18h 31, dec. −19° 16   mag. 6

Open cluster in Sagittarius about 2000 light years away. Contains a number of widely scattered bright stars one of which is a classical Delta-Cephei star. Use a medium telescope at low power. *(July)*

M 26, NGC 6694   r.a. 18h 44, dec. −09° 25   mag. 9

Open cluster in Scutum. *(July)*

Open Cluster with nebulousity M 16, NGC 6611

Omega, Horseshoe or Swan Nebula M 17, NGC 6618

Trifid Nebula M 20, NGC 6514

Globular Cluster M 22, NGC 6656

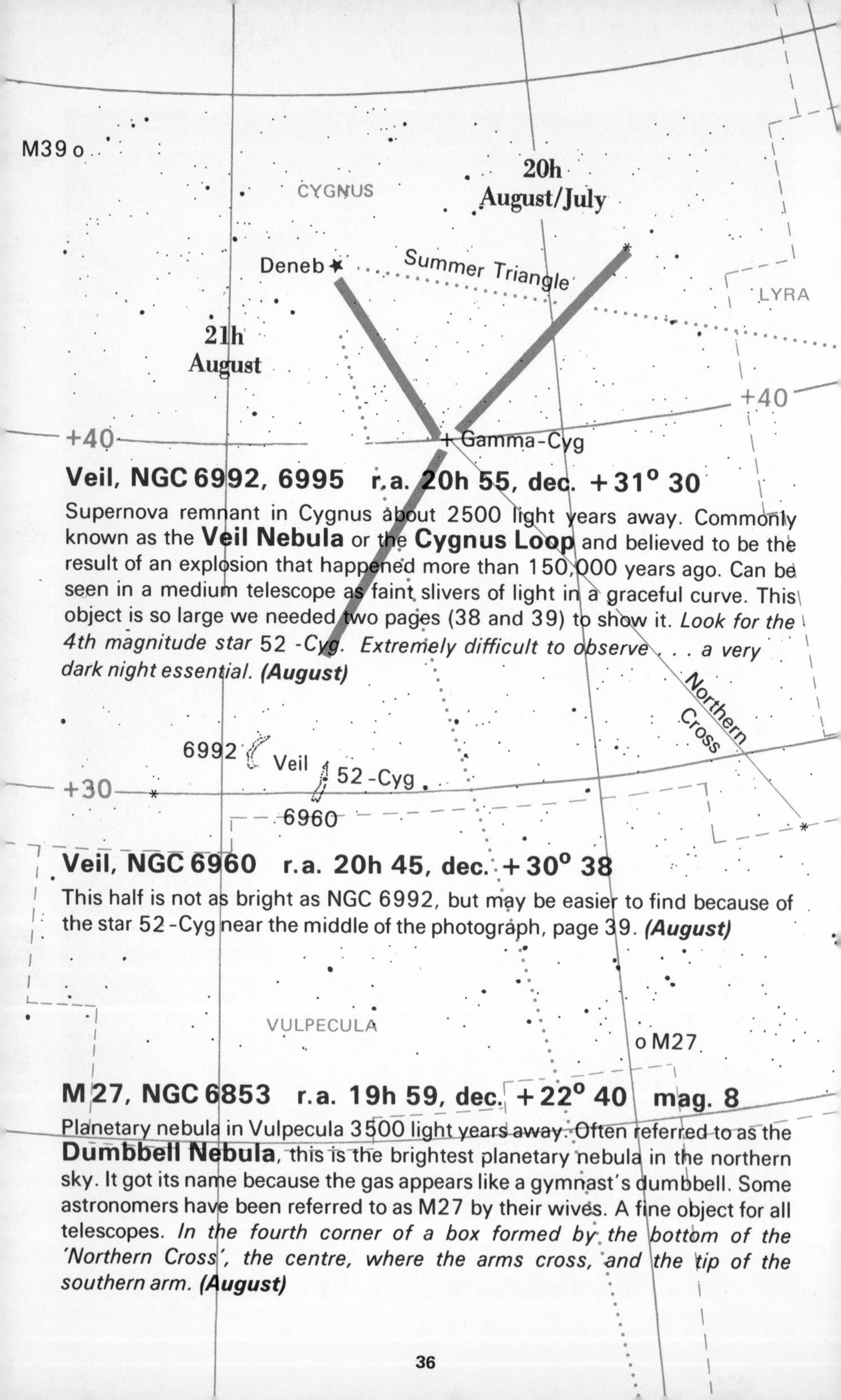

M39 o

CYGNUS

20h
August/July

Deneb ✷ .... Summer Triangle

LYRA

21h
August

+40

+40

+40 ————————————— + Gamma-Cyg

Veil, NGC 6992, 6995   r.a. 20h 55, dec. +31° 30

Supernova remnant in Cygnus about 2500 light years away. Commonly known as the **Veil Nebula** or the **Cygnus Loop** and believed to be the result of an explosion that happened more than 150,000 years ago. Can be seen in a medium telescope as faint slivers of light in a graceful curve. This object is so large we needed two pages (38 and 39) to show it. *Look for the 4th magnitude star 52 -Cyg. Extremely difficult to observe . . . a very dark night essential. (August)*

6992   Veil 52 -Cyg

+30

6960

Northern Cross

Veil, NGC 6960   r.a. 20h 45, dec. +30° 38

This half is not as bright as NGC 6992, but may be easier to find because of the star 52 -Cyg near the middle of the photograph, page 39. *(August)*

VULPECULA

o M27

M 27, NGC 6853   r.a. 19h 59, dec. +22° 40   mag. 8

Planetary nebula in Vulpecula 3500 light years away. Often referred to as the **Dumbbell Nebula**, this is the brightest planetary nebula in the northern sky. It got its name because the gas appears like a gymnast's dumbbell. Some astronomers have been referred to as M27 by their wives. A fine object for all telescopes. *In the fourth corner of a box formed by the bottom of the 'Northern Cross', the centre, where the arms cross, and the tip of the southern arm. (August)*

Dumbbell Planetary Nebula M 27, NGC 6853

Veil or Cygnus Loop Nebulae NGC 6992, 6995

Veil or Cygnus Loop Nebulae NGC 6960

Great Andromeda Nebula M 31, NGC 224

+ Gamma-And

1h
October

ANDROMEDA

+40

M32 ₀ ₀ M31

2h
November/October

0h
October/September

M 28, NGC 6626   r.a. 18h 23, dec. −24° 52   mag. 7
Globular Cluster in Sagittarius. *(July)*

M 29, NGC 6913   r.a. 20h 23, dec. +38° 27   mag. 8
Open Cluster in Cygnus.

M 30, NGC 7099   r.a. 21h 39, dec. −23° 15   mag. 8
Globular cluster in Capricornus. *(August)*

Elliptical Galaxy M 32, NGC 221

23h
September

22h
September/August

M 31, NGC 224   r.a. 0h 42, dec. +41° 09   mag. 4

Spiral galaxy with open arms more than 2 million light years away. The **Great Nebula in Andromeda** is one of the most spectacular naked eye sights in the night sky. On a dark night it will fill the entire field in a pair of binoculars. *Use the second 'V' of the 'W' in Casseopia as a pointer toward the 'Square' in Pegasus, see page 91. Or, follow the lower arm from the 'Square' to the third star, make a right turn and step out to where the third star should be. You will see M31 visually as a faint thumbprint. See page 42 for a more complete chart. (October)*

M 32, NGC 221   r.a. 0h 42, dec. +40° 45   mag. 9

Elliptical Galaxy in Andromeda, a companion of M31. Can be seen in the upper left-hand side of the photograph. *(October)*

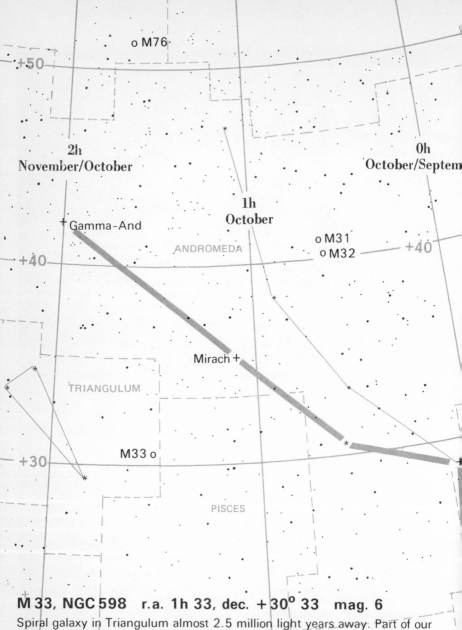

M 33, NGC 598   r.a. 1h 33, dec. +30° 33   mag. 6

Spiral galaxy in Triangulum almost 2.5 million light years away. Part of our Local Group of galaxies. Because of the large surface area the galaxy is quite dim and binoculars will give a better view than most telescopes. A large telescope will show the size best by gently rocking M33 in the field of view. This galaxy can also be seen on a really dark night with the unaided eye as a very faint patch of light. *About the same distance below the arm from the 'Square' in Pegasus as M31 is above it.* **(October)**

Spiral Galaxy with very open arms M 33, NGC 598

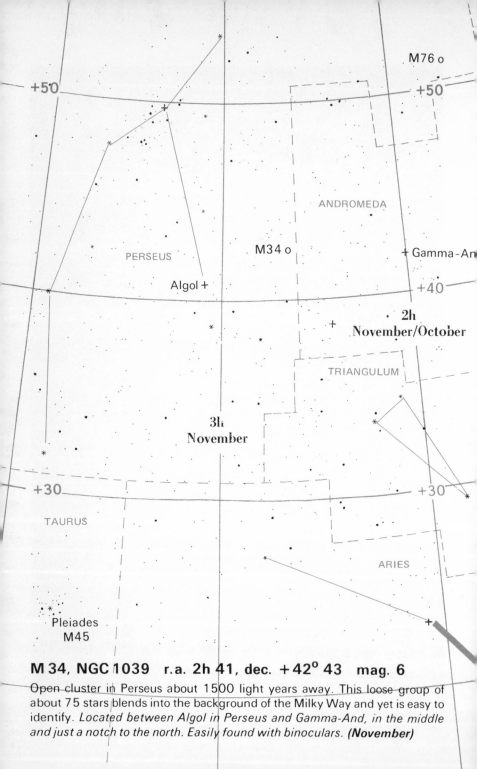

M 34, NGC 1039   r.a. 2h 41, dec. +42° 43   mag. 6

Open cluster in Perseus about 1500 light years away. This loose group of about 75 stars blends into the background of the Milky Way and yet is easy to identify. *Located between Algol in Perseus and Gamma-And, in the middle and just a notch to the north. Easily found with binoculars.* **(November)**

Open Cluster M 34, NGC 1039

M 35, NGC 2168   r.a. 6h 08, dec. +24° 21   mag. 6

Open cluster in Gemini under 3000 light years away. It can be seen clearly with binoculars. Low power will resolve it. Look for the compact open cluster known as NGC 2158 to the southwest. *(January)*

M 36, NGC 1960   r.a. 5h 35, dec. +34° 05   mag. 6

Open cluster in Auriga. Not shown in photographs, but can be found between M37 and M38. *(December)*

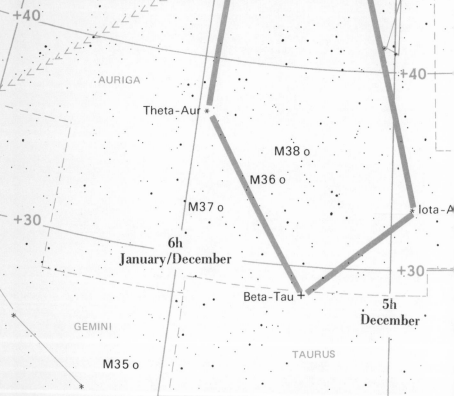

M 37, NGC 2099   r.a. 5h 52, dec. +32° 33   mag. 6

Open cluster in Auriga 4000 light years away. Estimated to be 200 million years old and is a striking object in a medium scope at low power. Stars are easily resolved. See photograph on page 48. *Between Beta-Tau and Theta-Aur, just outside the 'Pentagon'. (December)*

M 38, NGC 1912   r.a. 5h 27, dec. +35° 48   mag. 6

Open cluster in Auriga. Very large with a smaller companion NGC 1907 towards the bottom of the photograph on page 49. *Halfway between Theta-Aur and Iota-Aur. (December)*

Open Cluster M 35, NGC 2168

Open Cluster M 37, NGC 2099

Open Cluster M 38, NGC 1912

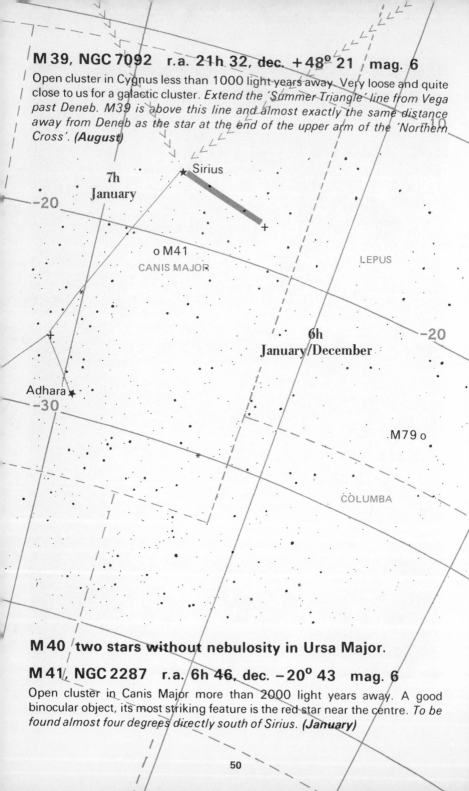

M 39, NGC 7092   r.a. 21h 32, dec. +48º 21   mag. 6

Open cluster in Cygnus less than 1000 light-years away. Very loose and quite close to us for a galactic cluster. *Extend the 'Summer Triangle' line from Vega past Deneb. M39 is above this line and almost exactly the same distance away from Deneb as the star at the end of the upper arm of the 'Northern Cross'. (August)*

Sirius

7h
January

−20

o M41

CANIS MAJOR

LEPUS

6h
January/December

−20

Adhara
−30

M79 o

COLUMBA

M 40 two stars without nebulosity in Ursa Major.

M 41, NGC 2287   r.a. 6h 46, dec. −20º 43   mag. 6

Open cluster in Canis Major more than 2000 light years away. A good binocular object, its most striking feature is the red star near the centre. *To be found almost four degrees directly south of Sirius. (January)*

Open Cluster M 41, NGC 2287

Orion's Belt, M 42, M 43 and the Horsehead taken with 200 mm telephoto lens

IC 434, Horsehead   r.a. 5h 39, dec. −02° 26

Dark nebula in Orion. Can be clearly seen in both photographs directly south of of Zeta-Ori. Extremely difficult to observe, even with a large telescope and dark skies. NGC 2024 just to the left of Zeta-Ori can be seen, but the dust lanes are extremely difficult because of the bright star in the same field. *Move south from Zeta-Ori and watch the triangles formed by the stars. It is easy to get to the right place, but tough to see the Horsehead. (December)*

Horsehead Nebula and Zeta-Ori

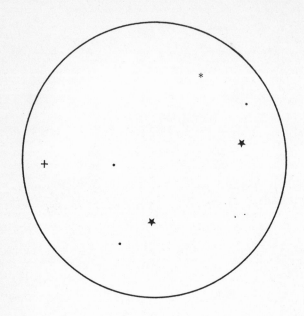

Trapezium

M 42, NGC 1976   r.a. 5h 34, dec. −05° 24

Diffuse nebula about 1500 light years away. Probably the most photo-graphed object in the northern sky, the **Great Nebula in Orion** is illuminated by the ultraviolet light from young hot stars exciting the hydrogen in the surrounding nebula. The object deserves detailed observation with all types of instruments. In the centre is Theta-Ori, a multiple star system also called the **Trapezium** because of the shape formed by its four main components. See the above diagram and compare with your own observation. Photographically this nebula appears reddish but when you observe it visually, however, it is a dull greenish tint. *Finder chart on page 96.* *(December)*

M 43, NGC 1982   r.a. 5h 35, dec. −05° 18

Diffuse nebula in Orion. Attached to the bottom of M42 in the photograph. *(December)*

Great Orion Nebula M 42, NGC 1976
Diffuse Nebula M 43, NGC 1982

Prasesepe or the Beehive taken with 200 mm telephoto lens

M 44, NGC 2632   r.a. 8h 39, dec. +20° 04   mag. 4

Open cluster in Cancer just over 500 light years away. Often called the **Beehive** or **Praesepe** and containing over 2500 stars, this naked eye cluster is rivalled only by the Pleiades. An unresolved fuzzy patch explodes into hundreds of stars with almost any instrument. *Halfway between Regulus and Pollux, Praesepe marks the centre of the constellation Cancer. (February)*

Praesepe or Beehive M 44, NGC 2632

M 45,   r.a. **3h 46,** dec. **+24° 03**   mag. 2   **Moon**

Open cluster in Taurus about 400 light years away. The **Pleiades** is one of the most delightful sights in the night sky, sometimes referred to as the **Seven Sisters**. The stars are surrounded by nebulosity as seen in the photographs. This is a reflection nebula as the stars appear to be only temporarily passing through this cloud of gas. This nebulosity can be seen in a medium telescope on a dark night. A pair of binoculars or a small telescope will reveal dozens of glittering stars of which over two hundred have been identified by astronomers. *Look north on a line with Orion's Belt, past Aldebaran and the Hyades. They can also be found by looking south from Perseus. See finder chart on page 44.* **(November)**

Pleiades or Seven Sisters M 45

M 46, NGC 2437   r.a. 7h 41, dec. −14° 46   mag. 7

Open cluster in Puppis about 5000 light years away. Rich concentration of stars famous for its planetary nebula, NGC 2438 which resembles the Ring Nebula on page 73. The nebula is not part of the cluster but about 300 light years closer to us. The cluster is located to the bottom right of the photograph and you can see the little ring of nebulosity to the upper left of this object. *Sweep ten degrees east of Sirius and a little north. (January)*

M 47, NGC 2422   r.a. 7h 36, dec. −14° 27   mag. 5

Open cluster in Puppis. A grouping of several bright stars easily located one degree west of M46. See photograph on page 62. This region is especially rich and a good area to observe with binoculars. *(January)*

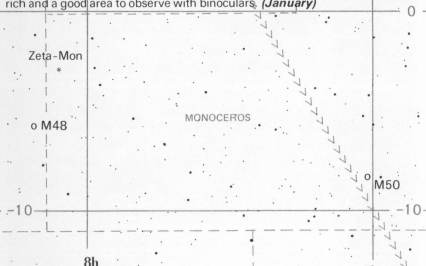

M 48, NGC 2548   r.a. 8h 13, dec. −05° 43   mag. 6

Open cluster in Hydra. Similar to M47, this is one of the 'lost' Messier objects that is well worth observing, even with a small telescope. See page 63 for photograph. *About four degrees south and one degree east of Zeta-Mon. (February)*

Open Cluster M 46, NGC 2437

Open Cluster M 47, NGC 2422

Open Cluster M 48, NGC 2548

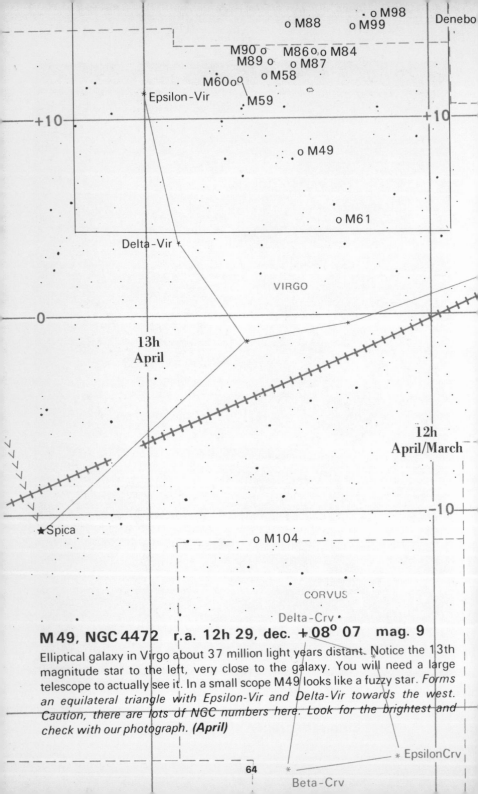

o M98

o M88   o M99   Denebo

M90 o   M86 o o M84

M89 o   o M87

M60 o o   o M58

★ Epsilon-Vir   M59

+10   +10

o M49

o M61

Delta-Vir ★

VIRGO

0

13h
April

12h
April/March

-10

★ Spica

o M104

CORVUS

Delta-Crv

M 49, NGC 4472   r.a. 12h 29, dec. +08° 07   mag. 9

Elliptical galaxy in Virgo about 37 million light years distant. Notice the 13th
magnitude star to the left, very close to the galaxy. You will need a large
telescope to actually see it. In a small scope M49 looks like a fuzzy star. *Forms
an equilateral triangle with Epsilon-Vir and Delta-Vir towards the west.
Caution, there are lots of NGC numbers here. Look for the brightest and
check with our photograph.* **(April)**

★ EpsilonCrv

★
Beta-Crv

Elliptical Galaxy M 49, NGC 4472

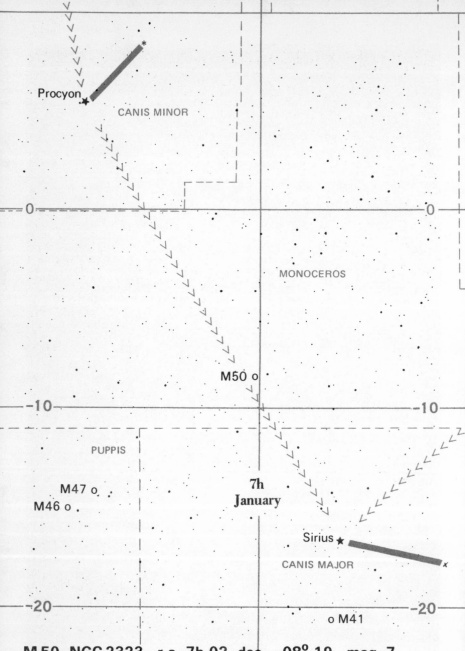

M 50, NGC 2323   r.a. 7h 02, dec. −08° 19   mag. 7

Open cluster in Monoceros about 2500 light years away. Very near to the galactic equator looking away from the nucleus of our Milky Way galaxy. There are about 100 stars in this cluster and it is an easy object for binoculars. *On a line one-third of the way from Sirius to Procyon.* **(January)**

Open Cluster M 50, NGC 2323

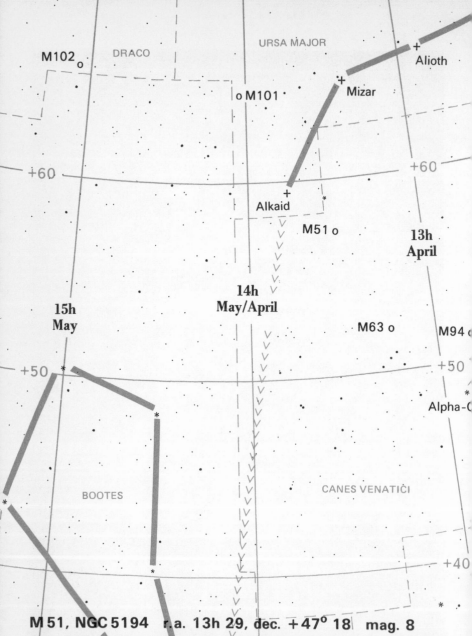

M 51, NGC 5194 r.a. 13h 29, dec. +47° 18 mag. 8

Spiral Galaxy with very open arms in Canes Venatici about 14 million light years away. The **Whirlpool Nebula** is one of the most beautiful objects for the amateur telescope. A small instrument will show two separate patches of light. A medium scope will allow you to trace the spiral arms for more than one full turn. *Easily located off Alkaid, the end star in the 'Dipper' handle. Form a triangle with the only other 4th magnitude star in the area. (April)*

Whirlpool Nebula M 51, NGC 5194

CYGNUS

M 52, NGC 7654   r.a. 23h 23, dec. +61° 29   mag. 7

Open cluster in Cassiopeia comprising more than 100 stars. *On a line beyond Alpha-Cas and Beta-Cas about the same distance above the 'W'. See page 120 for finder chart. (September)*

M 53, NGC 5024   r.a. 13h 12, dec. +18° 17   mag. 8

Globular cluster in Coma Berenices 6500 light years away. Slightly larger than M3. High power on any amateur telescope will only resolve it around the edges. *About one degree north of a line from Arcturus to Denebola, slightly closer to Arcturus. Watch out for the other cluster NGC 5053 to the west and slightly south. See page 16 for finder chart. (April)*

M 54, NGC 6715   r.a. 18h 54, dec. −30° 30   mag. 8

Globular cluster in Sagittarius. A medium telescope will not resolve its compactness. *Inside the 'Teapot', near the handle on the base. See page 22 for finder chart. (July)*

M 55, NGC 6809   r.a. 19h 39, dec. −31° 00   mag. 6

Globular cluster in Sagittarius about 20,000 light years away. Large and bright, much like M13, page 27. Very low and not easily resolved from northern latitudes. *Twice the distance from Sigma-Sgr and Tau-Sgr, on a line south from the handle of the 'Teapot'. See page 22 for finder chart. (July)*

o
M29

Northern Cross

Summer Triangle

+

19h
July

Vega

+30

LYRA

20h
August/July

M57

VULPECULA

Gamma-Lyr

o M56

Beta-Cyg

M 56, NGC 6779   r.a. 19h 16, dec. +30° 08   mag. 8

Globular cluster in Lyra 40,000 light years away. This very compact round cluster could have been easily mistaken for a comet. A small telescope will show it well. A large telescope will only begin to resolve the outer stars. *Look halfway between Gamma-Lyr and Beta-Cyg. (July)*

Globular Cluster M 56, NGC 6779

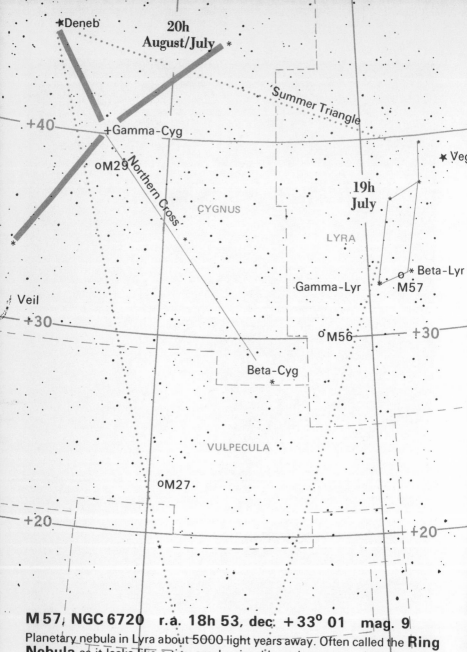

M 57, NGC 6720   r.a. 18h 53, dec. +33° 01   mag. 9

Planetary nebula in Lyra about 5000 light years away. Often called the **Ring Nebula** as it looks like a tiny smoke ring blown into space. Actually it is a shell of gas drifting away from a central star. Because we are looking through more gas at the edge of the sphere than through the centre, it appears as a ring. A small telescope will easily show the ring, however a large telescope is required to reveal the 14th magnitude star in the central core. *Find the Ring midway between Gamma-Lyr and Beta-Lyr.* **(July)**

Ring Nebula M 57, NGC 6720

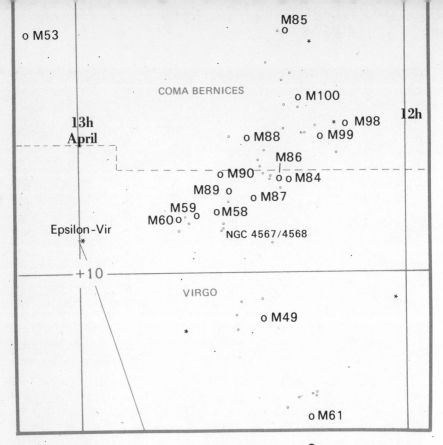

M 58, NGC 4579   r.a. 12h 37, dec. +11° 56   mag. 10

Spiral galaxy in Virgo. M58 is in the upper right corner of the picture. Pictured near the centre are two colliding galaxies, NGC 4568 and 4567. While this would appear to be catastrophic, the chance of interstellar collision is remote because of the enormous distances involved. We only know of the collision because of the radio noise generated by the interstellar gases rushing against each other. NGC 4564 is to the right, near the centre of the picture. In this area are more than 13,000 galaxies often referred to as the **Virgo Cluster**. See page 64 for finder chart. *(April)*

M 59, NGC 4621   r.a. 12h 41, dec. +11° 47   mag. 10

Elliptical Galaxy in Virgo just east of M58, see page 76. *(April)*

M 60, NGC 4649   r.a. 12h 43, dec. +11° 41   mag. 9

Elliptical Galaxy in Virgo in the same field as M59, page 76. *(April)*

M 61, NGC 4303   r.a. 12h 21, dec. +04° 36   mag. 10

Spiral galaxy in Virgo with very open arms. This is the most southerly member of the Virgo Cluster. Spiral arms are visible with a large telescope, page 77. *(April)*

Barred spiral galaxy with open arms M 58, NGC 4579
Colliding galaxies NGC 4567 and 4568

Elliptical Galaxy M 59, NGC 4621
Elliptical Galaxy M 60, NGC 4649

Spiral Galaxy with very open arms M 61, NGC 4303

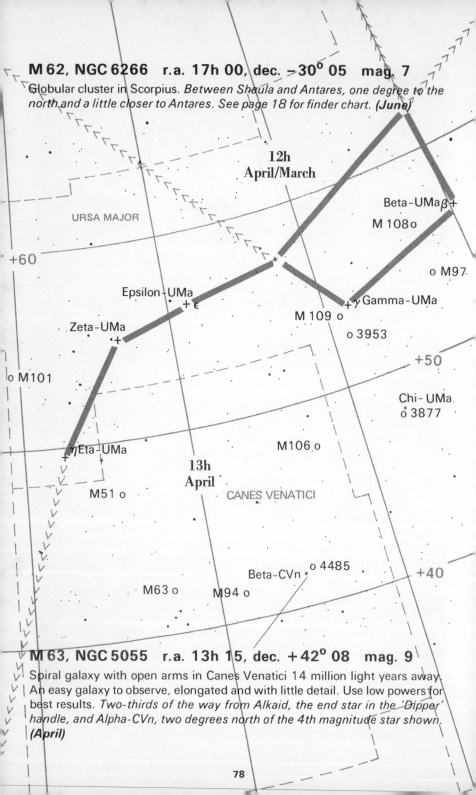

M 62, NGC 6266   r.a. 17h 00, dec. −30° 05   mag. 7

Globular cluster in Scorpius. *Between Shaula and Antares, one degree to the north and a little closer to Antares. See page 18 for finder chart. (June)*

12h
April/March

Beta-UMaβ +

M 108 o

URSA MAJOR

+60

o M97

Epsilon-UMa
+ ε

Gamma-UMa
+ γ

M 109 o

Zeta-UMa
·+

o 3953

o M101

+50

Chi-UMa
o 3877

η Eta-UMa
+

M106 o

13h
April

M51 o

CANES VENATICI

o 4485

Beta-CVn *

+40

M63 o

M94 o

M 63, NGC 5055   r.a. 13h 15, dec. +42° 08   mag. 9

Spiral galaxy with open arms in Canes Venatici 14 million light years away. An easy galaxy to observe, elongated and with little detail. Use low powers for best results. *Two-thirds of the way from Alkaid, the end star in the 'Dipper' handle, and Alpha-CVn, two degrees north of the 4th magnitude star shown. (April)*

Spiral Galaxy with open arms M 63, NGC 5055

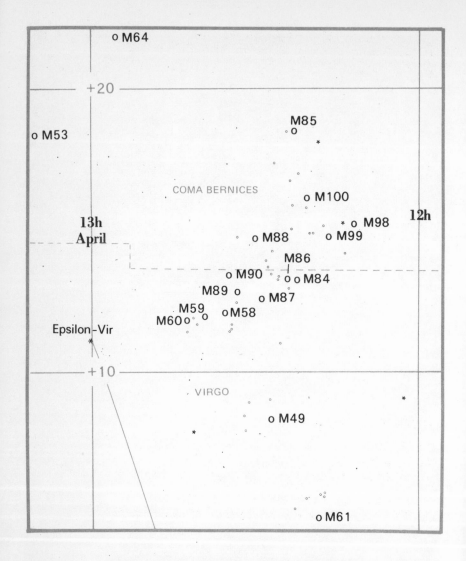

Coma and Virgo Cluster of Galaxies

M 64, NGC 4826   r.a. 12h 56, dec. +21° 48   mag. 9

Spiral galaxy with open arms in Coma Berenices about 12 million light years away. The **Black-Eye Nebula** is large and bright, slightly oval with a dark central dust lane giving it its name. The dark spot is difficult to observe in a small telescope. The most northern member of the Coma Cluster on our chart. *(April)*

Black-Eye Nebula M 64, NGC 4826

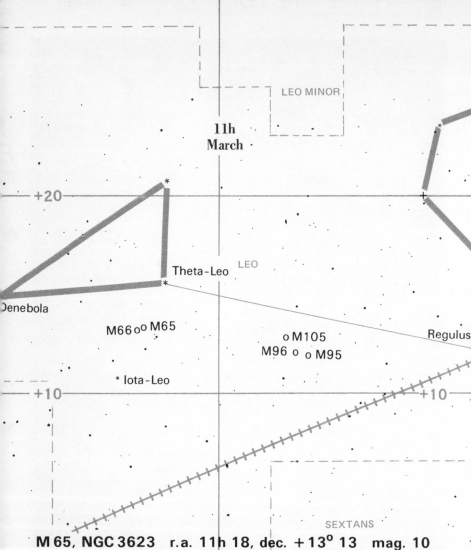

LEO MINOR

11h
March

LEO

Theta-Leo

Denebola

M66 oo M65

o M105
M96 o o M95

Regulus

* Iota-Leo

+10

+10

SEXTANS

M 65, NGC 3623   r.a. 11h 18, dec. +13° 13   mag. 10

Spiral galaxy in Leo about 20 million light years away. Look to the bottom right in the photograph. Astronomers estimate M65 to be over 100 times as large as our own Milky Way Galaxy. *Find this small grouping of galaxies between Theta-Leo and Iota-Leo.* *(March)*

M 66, NGC 3627   r.a. 11h 19, dec. +13° 07   mag. 9

Spiral galaxy with open arms in Leo. Look to the bottom left in the photograph. Blocks of obscuring dust can be observed with a medium telescope. Near the top of the photograph, NGC 3628 is an edge-on spiral galaxy too dim for Messier to observe. An easy target for a medium telescope. Just to the west of our picture field, NGC 3593 can also be seen. *(March)*

Spiral Galaxy M 65, NGC 3623
Spiral Galaxy with open arms M 66, NGC 3627

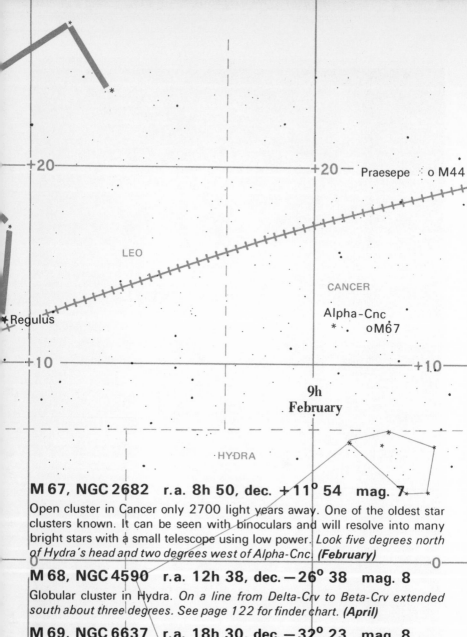

+20 +20 — Praesepe ○ M44

LEO

CANCER

Alpha-Cnc

✳ ○ M67

✳ Regulus

+10 +10

9h
February

HYDRA

M 67, NGC 2682   r.a. 8h 50, dec. +11° 54   mag. 7

Open cluster in Cancer only 2700 light years away. One of the oldest star clusters known. It can be seen with binoculars and will resolve into many bright stars with a small telescope using low power. *Look five degrees north of Hydra's head and two degrees west of Alpha-Cnc. (February)*

0 0

M 68, NGC 4590   r.a. 12h 38, dec. −26° 38   mag. 8

Globular cluster in Hydra. *On a line from Delta-Crv to Beta-Crv extended south about three degrees. See page 122 for finder chart. (April)*

M 69, NGC 6637   r.a. 18h 30, dec. −32° 23   mag. 8

Globular cluster in Sagittarius. *About three degrees west of M70 toward the spout of the 'Teapot'. See page 22 for finder chart. (July)*

M 70, NGC 6681   r.a. 18h 42, dec. −32° 18   mag. 8

Globular cluster in Sagittarius. Very similar to M69. *In the middle of a line joining the bottom of the 'Teapot'. See page 22 for finder chart. (July)*

Open Cluster M 67, NGC 2682

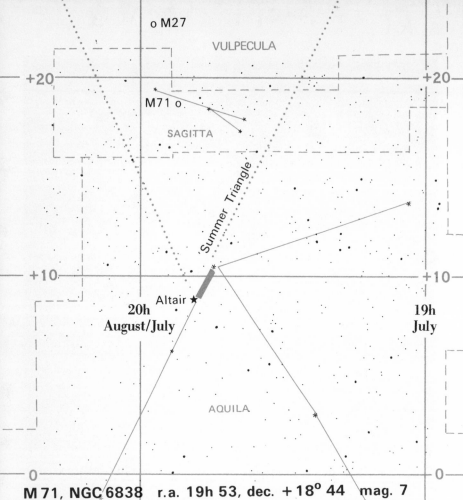

o M27

VULPECULA

+20

M71 o

SAGITTA

Summer Triangle

+10

Altair ★

20h
August/July

19h
July

AQUILA

0

M 71, NGC 6838   r.a. 19h 53, dec. + 18° 44   mag. 7

Globular cluster in Sagitta probably very remote in our galaxy. Because of its brightness, most small telescopes with high powers will give some resolution. *Just south of a line joining the tip of the 'Arrow' in Sagitta with its feathers. South of Cygnus, within the 'Summer Triangle' the arrow points to the 'Square' in Pegasus. (July)*

* Lambda-

M 72, NGC 6981   r.a. 20h 53, dec. − 12° 39   mag. 9

Globular cluster in Aquarius. Small with no unusual features. A medium telescope will not resolve this one. *Look one degree east and three degrees south of Epsilon-Aqr. See page 14 for finder chart. (August)*

M 73, NGC 6994   r.a. 20h 58, dec. − 12° 44

Four undistinguished stars in Aquarius usually omitted from Messier's Catalogue. You may wonder which three or four stars were intended. Perhaps Messier saw the **Saturn Nebula**, NGC 7009, which is just over one degree to the north-east. See page 14 for finder chart. *(August)*

Globular Cluster M 71, NGC 6838

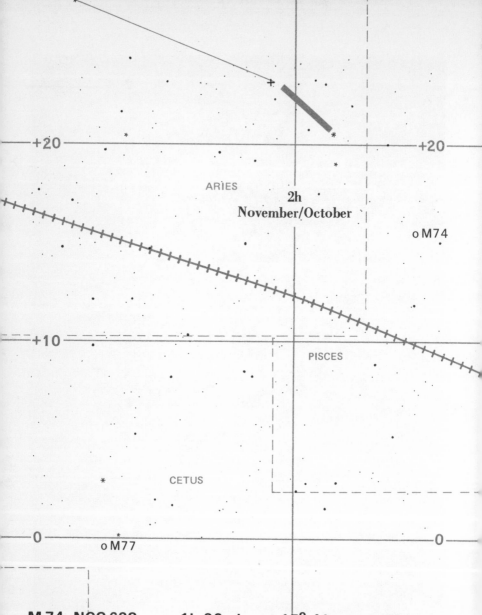

+20

+20

ARIES

2h
November/October

o M74

+10

+10

PISCES

CETUS

0

0

o M77

M74, NGC628   r.a. 1h 36, dec. +15° 41   mag. 10

Spiral galaxy with very open arms in Pisces. A very low surface brightness due to its huge size. It is estimated to have over 50 billion stars in its composition and is tilted 55 degrees to our line of sight. Dreyer wrongly classified M74 in his NGC catalogue as it looked to him like an unresolved globular cluster. *Look for the three bright stars in Aries and find the fourth magnitude Eta-Psc. M74 is about one and a half degrees east and a little north of this star.* **(October)**

Spiral Galaxy with very open arms M 74, NGC 628

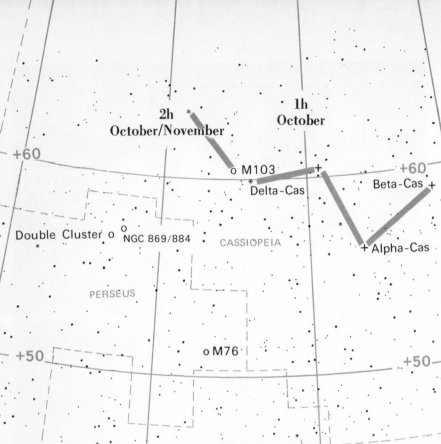

2h
October/November
1h
October

+60   +60

o M103
*
Delta-Cas   Beta-Cas   +

Double Cluster o o NGC 869/884   CASSIOPEIA
*
+ Alpha-Cas

PERSEUS

o M76

+50   +50

M 75, NGC 6864 r.a. 20h 04 dec. — 21° 59 mag. 8

Globular cluster in Sagittarius. Small but bright and easy to locate as it is in a rather blank area of sky. A medium telescope will not resolve the stars in it. See page 94 for finder chart. *(July)*

M 76, NGC 650 r.a. 1h 41, dec. +51° 28 mag. 11

Planetary nebula in Perseus about 15,000 light years away. Messier saw the **Little Dumbbell** as a nebulous cluster, William Herschel thought it to be a double nebula and Lord Rosse identified it as a spiral nebula. Its name comes from the resemblance to M27, the Dumbbell Nebula, page 37. A good challenge for a small telescope, it will bear medium to high powers. Using a large telescope, it appears to be a bright bar only slightly thinner in the middle. *Locate the 4th magnitude Phi-Per and look one degree north. (October)*

NGC 869, 884 r.a. 2h 18, dec. +57° 04 mag. 10

Double cluster in Perseus about 7500 light years away. Containing over 600 stars this giant double cluster is one of the most spectacular naked eye objects in the northern sky, see page 92. *(November)*

Little Dumbbell Planetary Nebula M 76, NGC 650

Double Cluster in Perseus

Supernova in Galaxy NGC 4414, 1974

Galaxy NGC 4414, 1977

NGC 4414 r.a. 12h 25, dec. +31° 22

Supernova in a remote galaxy in Coma Berenices. Every so often a deep sky object becomes of particular interest to astronomers. In the spring of 1974 a supernova ripped through NGC 4414, a rather ordinary spiral galaxy. One tiny star, with a cataclysmic explosion, destroyed itself and released enough energy to rival the output of the entire galaxy. In a few short months the star shrunk back into oblivion as shown in a recent photograph. This is what happened to M1 in our own galaxy. *(April)*

Altair

AQUILA

0 ——————————————————— 0

20h
August/July

M 77, NGC 1068   r.a. 2h 42, dec. −00° 04   mag. 9

Spiral galaxy with open arms in Cetus. The brightest object in a cluster of about 45 galaxies, six of which are good objects with a medium telescope. This giant galaxy is over 500 times bigger than our own. In a small telescope it looks like a fuzzy star, a larger telescope will reveal it true roundish shape. *Look for the 4th magnitude Delta-Cet on the southern corner of an equilateral triangle formed by the Pleiades and the main stars of Aries. M77 is east and a little to the south of Delta-Cet. **(November)*** *See page 88 for finder chart.*

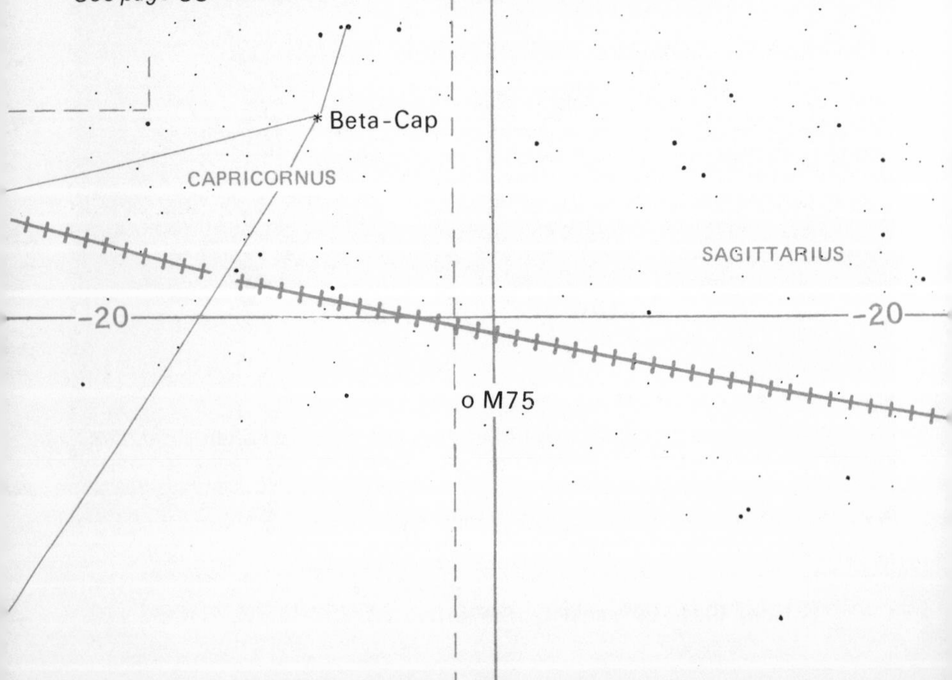

* Beta-Cap

CAPRICORNUS

SAGITTARIUS

−20 ——————————————————— −20

o M75

Spiral Galaxy with open arms M 77, NGC 1068

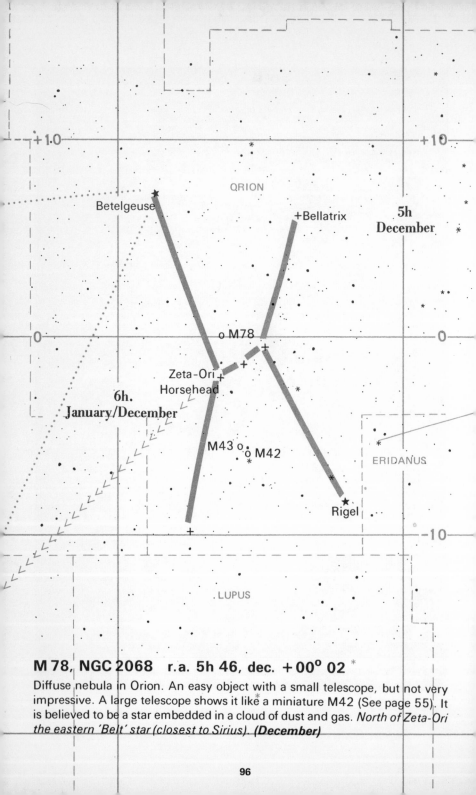

ORION

+1.0   +10

Betelgeuse

5h
December
+Bellatrix

0   o M78   0

Zeta-Ori +
Horsehead

6h.
January/December

M43 o o M42

ERIDANUS

Rigel   -10

LUPUS

M 78, NGC 2068   r.a. 5h 46, dec. +00° 02 *

Diffuse nebula in Orion. An easy object with a small telescope, but not very impressive. A large telescope shows it like a miniature M42 (See page 55). It is believed to be a star embedded in a cloud of dust and gas. *North of Zeta-Ori the eastern 'Belt' star (closest to Sirius).* **(December)**

Diffuse Nebula M 78, NGC 2068

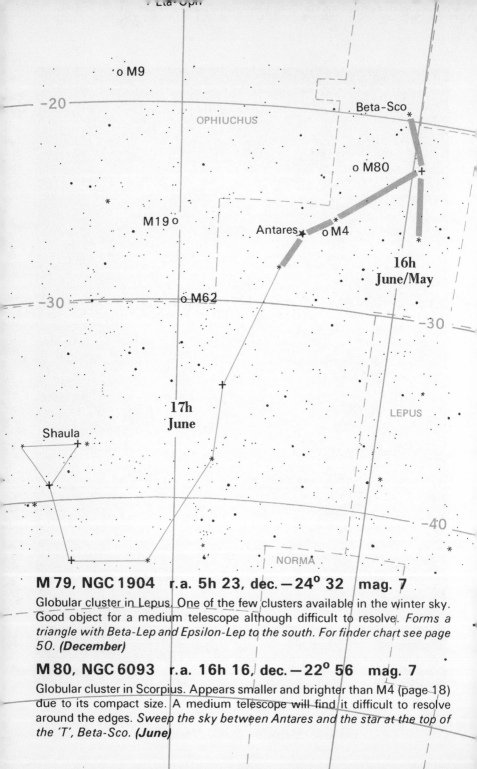

M 79, NGC 1904   r.a. 5h 23, dec. −24° 32   mag. 7

Globular cluster in Lepus. One of the few clusters available in the winter sky. Good object for a medium telescope although difficult to resolve. *Forms a triangle with Beta-Lep and Epsilon-Lep to the south. For finder chart see page 50. (December)*

M 80, NGC 6093   r.a. 16h 16, dec. −22° 56   mag. 7

Globular cluster in Scorpius. Appears smaller and brighter than M4 (page 18) due to its compact size. A medium telescope will find it difficult to resolve around the edges. *Sweep the sky between Antares and the star at the top of the 'T', Beta-Sco. (June)*

Global Cluster M 80, NGC 6093

Polaris

M 81, NGC 3031   r.a. 9h 54, dec. +69° 09   mag. 7

Spiral galaxy with open arms in Ursa Major over 6 million light years away. This galaxy is seen by us at a 45-degree angle much like the famous Spiral Galaxy in Andromeda. A large telescope will show its spiral arms, but a small one will only reveal a fuzzy ball. *An easy way to find both M81 and M82 is to join a line diagonally across the bowl of the 'Dipper' from the bottom left star Phecda to the upper pointer Dubhe. Extend this line an equal distance northward and you will be very close to these galaxies. (February)*

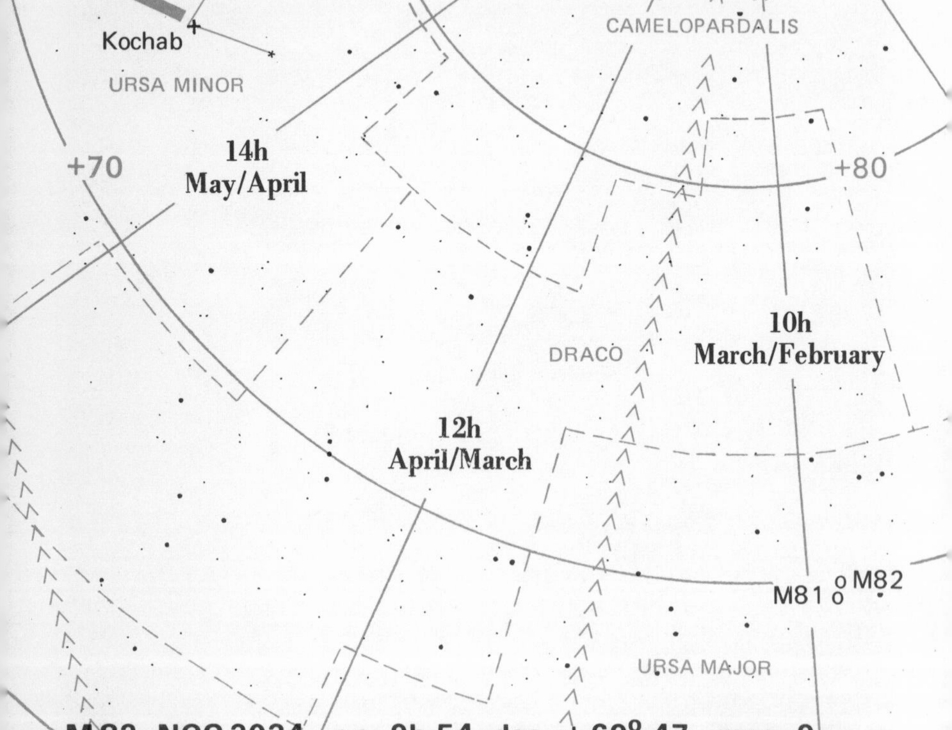

Kochab

CAMELOPARDALIS

URSA MINOR

+70

14h
May/April

+80

DRACO

10h
March/February

12h
April/March

M81 o M82

URSA MAJOR

M 82, NGC 3034   r.a. 9h 54, dec. +69° 47   mag. 9

Irregular galaxy in Ursa Major. In this galaxy there appears to have been a gigantic explosion which occurred over 1 million years ago, as seen from earth. In long exposure photography an enormous jet appears to be shooting out from the centre at tremendous velocity. This explosion is a strong radio source and may be effecting nearby M81. Both of these galaxies are the subject of modern research and many of their properties remain unexplained. *(February)*

+60

M 83, NGC 5236   r.a. 13h 36, dec. −29° 46   mag. 8

Spiral galaxy with very open arms in Hydra. From northern latitudes difficult to observe. *About equidistant between 2nd magnitude Theta-Cen and 3rd magnitude Gamma-Hya. (April) See page* 122 *for finder chart*

Spiral Galaxy with open arms M 81, NGC 3031
Irregular Galaxy M 82, NGC 3034

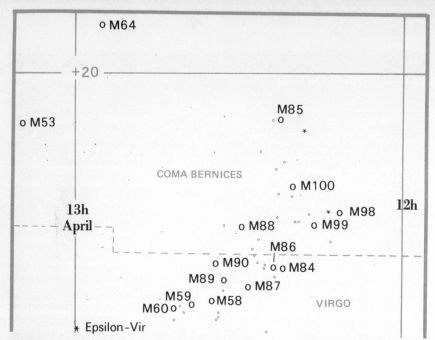

M 84, NGC 4374   r.a. 12h 24, dec. +13° 00   mag. 10

Elliptical galaxy in Virgo. Near the bottom of the photograph. *(April)*

M 85, NGC 4382   r.a. 12h 24, dec. +18° 18   mag. 10

Oval galaxy in Coma Berenices. Not shown in the photographs. *(April)*

M 86, NGC 4406   r.a. 12h 25, dec. +13° 03   mag. 10

Elliptical galaxy in Virgo. Toward the centre of the photograph, between NGC 4488 and 4402. Above and slightly to the right are NGC 4438 and 4435. *(April)*

M 87, NGC 4486   r.a. 12h 30, dec. +12° 30   mag. 9

Peculiar elliptical galaxy in Virgo. Noted for its many globular clusters. *See page 104. (April)*

M 88, NGC 4501   r.a. 12h 31, dec. +14° 32   mag. 10

Spiral galaxy with open arms in Coma Berenices. Not shown in photographs. *(April)*

M 89, NGC 4552   r.a. 12h 35, dec. +12° 40   mag. 10

Elliptical galaxy in Virgo. Shown near bottom of photograph on page 105. *(April)*

M 90, NGC 4569   r.a. 12h 36, dec. +13° 16   mag. 10

Spiral galaxy with open arms in Virgo on page 105 near the top. *(April)*

M 91 has never been seen again, could have been M58.

Elliptical Galaxy M 84, NGC 4374
Elliptical Galaxy M 86, NGC 4406

Peculiar Elliptical Galaxy M 87, NGC 4486

Elliptical Galaxy M 89, NGC 4552
Spiral Galaxy with open arms M 90, NGC 4569

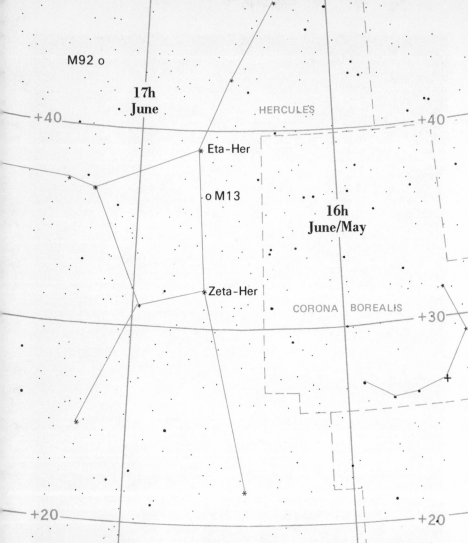

M 92, NGC 6341   r.a. 17h 17, dec. +43° 10   mag. 6

Globular cluster in Hercules over 28,000 light years away. Frequently overlooked because of its more popular companion M13. It is nearly as bright and contains about 200,000 solar masses. A striking object in any telescope, it will not resolve in a small telescope, but appears as a fuzzy ball. *About two-fifths of the way from Iota-Her to Eta-Her. (June)*

M 93, NGC 2447   r.a. 7h 44, dec. −23° 49   mag. 6

Open cluster in Puppis. Shows well with a small instrument and low powers. *Located about 2 degrees northwest of Xi-Pup. See finder chart, page 60. (January)*

Globular Cluster M 92, NGC 6341

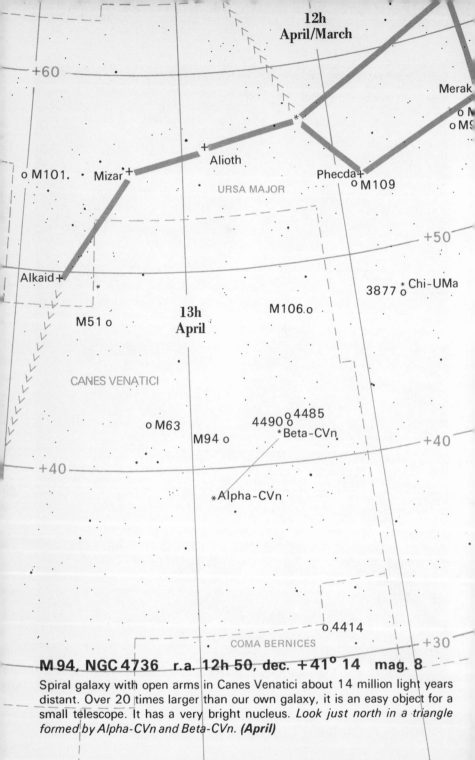

+60

Merak

o M
o M9

*

Alioth

Mizar +

o M101 .

URSA MAJOR

Phecda+
o M109

+50

Alkaid +

*

3877 o * Chi-UMa

M51 o

13h
April

M106 o

CANES VENATICI

o M63

4490 o o 4485
* Beta-CVn

M94 o

+40

+40

*Alpha-CVn

o 4414

COMA BERNICES

+30

M 94, NGC 4736 r.a. 12h 50, dec. +41° 14   mag. 8

Spiral galaxy with open arms in Canes Venatici about 14 million light years
distant. Over 20 times larger than our own galaxy, it is an easy object for a
small telescope. It has a very bright nucleus. *Look just north in a triangle
formed by Alpha-CVn and Beta-CVn. (April)*

Spiral Galaxy with open arms M 94, NGC 4736

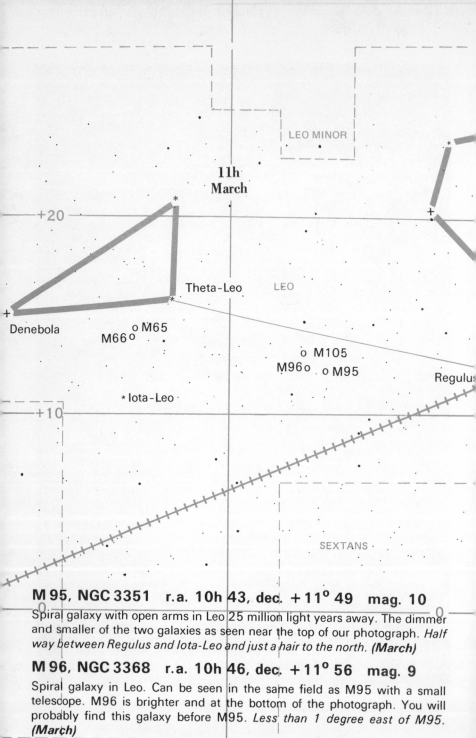

LEO MINOR

11h
March

+20

Theta-Leo   LEO

Denebola
M66 o   o M65

o M105
M96 o   o M95

Regulus

* Iota-Leo

+10

SEXTANS

M 95, NGC 3351   r.a. 10h 43, dec. +11° 49   mag. 10

Spiral galaxy with open arms in Leo 25 million light years away. The dimmer and smaller of the two galaxies as seen near the top of our photograph. *Half way between Regulus and Iota-Leo and just a hair to the north. (March)*

M 96, NGC 3368   r.a. 10h 46, dec. +11° 56   mag. 9

Spiral galaxy in Leo. Can be seen in the same field as M95 with a small telescope. M96 is brighter and at the bottom of the photograph. You will probably find this galaxy before M95. *Less than 1 degree east of M95. (March)*

Barred Spiral Galaxy with open arms M 95, NGC 3351
Spiral Galaxy M 96, NGC 3368

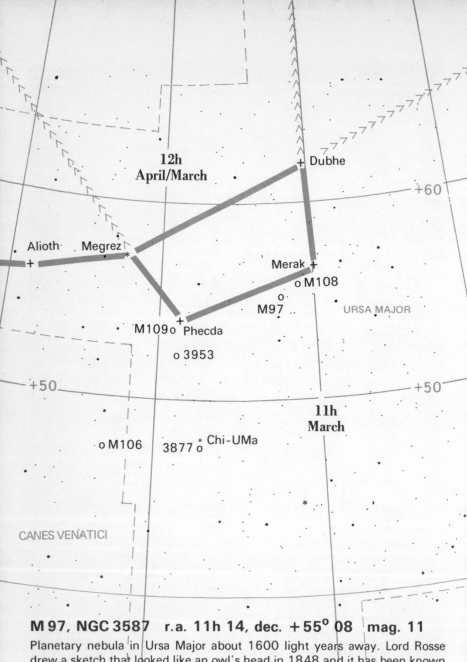

M 97, NGC 3587   r.a. 11h 14, dec. +55° 08   mag. 11

Planetary nebula in Ursa Major about 1600 light years away. Lord Rosse drew a sketch that looked like an owl's head in 1848 and it has been known as the **Owl Nebula** ever since. The two dark patches that appear as the owl's eyes are caused by an unequal distribution of gas. Be sure to use low power as high power adds nothing. The central star in the owl's beak is easily photographed, but extremely difficult to observe. *A hazy patch of light about 2 degrees southeast of Merak, the southern pointer of the 'Dipper'.* **(March)**

Owl Planetary Nebula M 97, NGC 3587

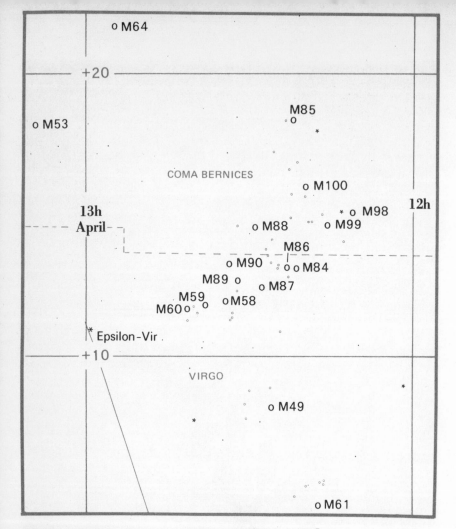

M 98, NGC 4192   r.a. 12h 13, dec. +15° 01   mag. 10

Spiral galaxy with open arms in Coma Berenices. Set your telescope on Denebola, switch off the clock drive and wait. In about 25 minutes M98 will drift into view and you can start your tour of the Coma Cluster. *(April)*

M 99, NGC 4254   r.a. 12h 18, dec. +14° 32   mag. 10

Spiral galaxy with very open arms in Coma Berenices. A large telescope reveals dark blotches of dust silhouetted against a light haze. *Sweep gently to the south east about one-half degree from M98. See page 116. (April)*

M 100, NGC 4321   r.a. 12h 22, dec. +15° 56   mag. 10

Spiral galaxy with very open arms in Coma Berenices estimated to be 40 million light years away. *Almost straight north from M99 about three full-moon widths. See page 117. (April)*

Spiral Galaxy with open arms M 98, NGC 4192

Spiral Galaxy with very open arms M 99, NGC 4254

Spiral Galaxy with very open arms M 100, NGC 4321

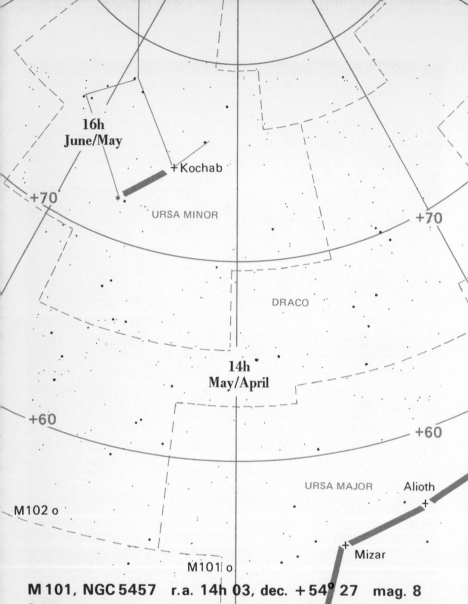

+Kochab

URSA MINOR

DRACO

14h
May/April

+70

+70

+60

+60

URSA MAJOR   Alioth
+

M102 o

M101 o

+ Mizar

M 101, NGC 5457   r.a. 14h 03, dec. +54° 27   mag. 8

Spiral galaxy with very open arms in Ursa Major about 14 million light years away. One of the finest examples of a face-on spiral. Despite its published magnitude, its surface brightness is very low making it a fairly hard object to locate. It looks like a hazy silver dollar at arm's length through a large telescope. It can also be seen in binoculars on a very dark night. M101 gives one excellent experience at locating other faint objects in the sky. *Visualize an equilateral triangle using the last two stars in the handle of the 'Dipper', Mizar and Alkaid. Find the third point of the triangle directly north of these stars and observe a dim patch of light.* *(May)*

Spiral Galaxy with very open arms M 101, NGC 5457

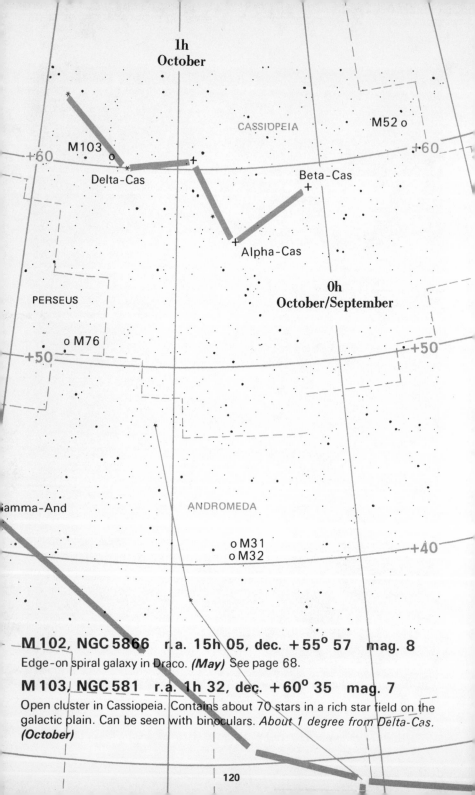

1h
October

CASSIOPEIA

M52 o

+60

+60

M103 o

Beta-Cas
+

Delta-Cas

Alpha-Cas
+

PERSEUS

0h
October/September

o M76

+50

+50

Gamma-And

ANDROMEDA

o M31
o M32

+40

M 102, NGC 5866 r.a. 15h 05, dec. +55° 57 mag. 8
Edge-on spiral galaxy in Draco. *(May)* See page 68.

M 103, NGC 581 r.a. 1h 32, dec. +60° 35 mag. 7
Open cluster in Cassiopeia. Contains about 70 stars in a rich star field on the galactic plain. Can be seen with binoculars. *About 1 degree from Delta-Cas. (October)*

Open Cluster M 103, NGC 581

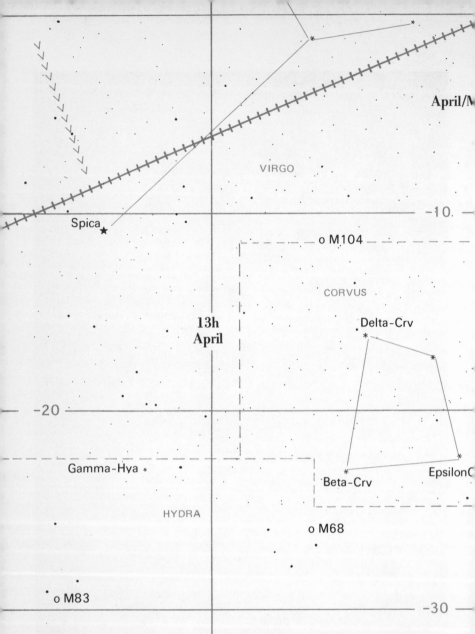

April/M

VIRGO

Spica

o M104

CORVUS

Delta-Crv

13h
April

-10.

-20

Gamma-Hya

Beta-Crv

EpsilonC

HYDRA

o M68

o M83

-30

M 104, NGC 4594   r.a. 12h 37, dec. −11° 21   mag. 8

Spiral galaxy with open arms in Virgo 37 million light years away. At this incredible distance the **Sombrero Nebula** can be seen easily. The dark band can be clearly seen with a medium telescope. It is an excellent example of an edge-on galaxy and quite striking. Use averted vision for a really clear view. *Take a line from Epsilon-Crv to Delta-Crv and extend it north about two-thirds of the distance. (April)*

Sombrero Nebula M 104, NGC 4594

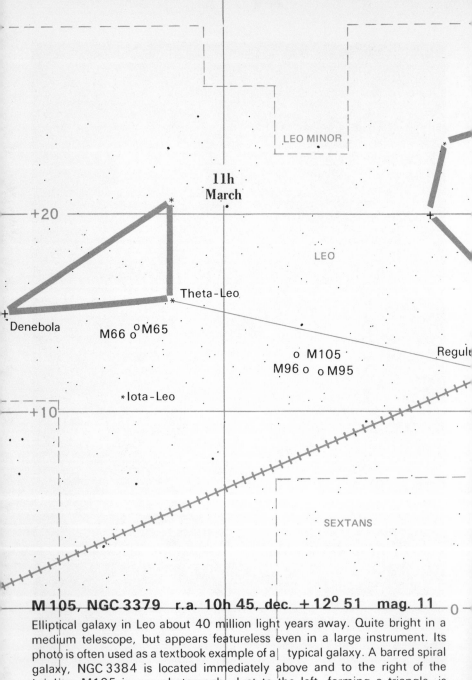

LEO MINOR

11h
March

+20

LEO

Theta-Leo

Denebola   M66 o°M65

o M105
M96 o o M95

Regulu

*Iota-Leo

+10

SEXTANS

M 105, NGC 3379   r.a. 10h 45, dec. +12° 51   mag. 11

Elliptical galaxy in Leo about 40 million light years away. Quite bright in a
medium telescope, but appears featureless even in a large instrument. Its
photo is often used as a textbook example of a typical galaxy. A barred spiral
galaxy, NGC 3384 is located immediately above and to the right of the
brighter M105 in our photograph. Just to the left, forming a triangle, is
NGC 3389, a very open-armed spiral galaxy *One-third of the way from*
Regulus to Denebola, just above M96. (March)

Elliptical Galaxy M 105, NGC 3379
Elliptical Galaxy NGC 3384, Spiral Galaxy NGC 3389

M 106, NGC 4258   r.a. 12h 17, dec. +47° 35   mag. 10

Spiral galaxy with open arms in Canes Venatici about 14 million light years away. This galaxy is over 100 times as massive as our own Milky Way. An easy object for a small telescope.   Note NGC 4217 an edge-on sprial galaxy in the lower right corner   *(April)*

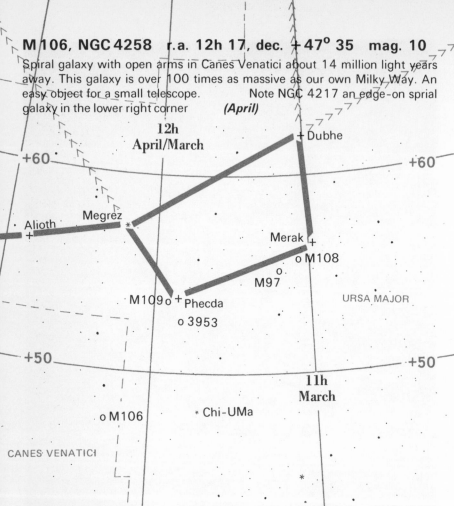

M 107, NGC 6171   r.a. 16h 30, dec. −12° 57   mag. 10

Globular cluster in Ophiuchus. *About 2 degrees southwest of Zeta-Oph. See page 24 for finder chart. (June)*

M 108, NGC 3556   r.a. 11h 09, dec. +55° 57   mag. 11

Spiral galaxy with open arms in Ursa Major about 25 million light years away. Contains enough material to make 14 billion of our own suns. Dark obscuring dust patches can be clearly seen in a medium telescope. *Located one and a half degrees southeast of Merak, in the 'Dipper'. (March)*

M 109, NGC 3992   r.a. 11h 55, dec. +53° 39   mag. 11

Barred spiral galaxy with very open arms in Ursa Major. Appears as a bright nucleus surrounded by a dim halo. *Found in the same low-power field as Phecda in the bowl of the 'Dipper'. (March)*

Spiral Galaxy with open arms M 106, NGC 4258

Spiral Galaxy with open arms M 108, NGC 3556

**Barred Spiral Galaxy with very open arms M 109,
NGC 3992**

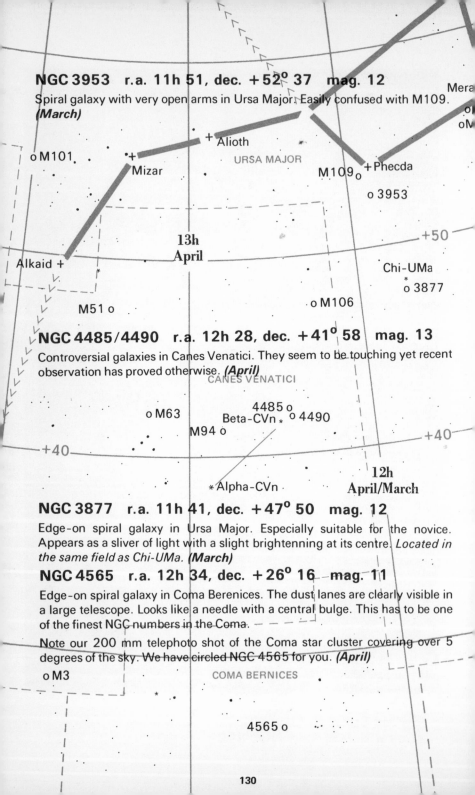

NGC 3953   r.a. 11h 51, dec. +52° 37   mag. 12

Spiral galaxy with very open arms in Ursa Major. Easily confused with M109. *(March)*

Mera

o
oM

+ Alioth

URSA MAJOR

o M101   + Mizar

M109 o   + Phecda

o 3953

13h
April

+50

Chi-UMa

o 3877

Alkaid +

M51 o

o M106

NGC 4485/4490   r.a. 12h 28, dec. +41° 58   mag. 13

Controversial galaxies in Canes Venatici. They seem to be touching yet recent observation has proved otherwise. *(April)*

CANES VENATICI

o M63

4485 o
Beta-CVn * o 4490

M94 o

+40

+40

* Alpha-CVn

12h
April/March

NGC 3877   r.a. 11h 41, dec. +47° 50   mag. 12

Edge-on spiral galaxy in Ursa Major. Especially suitable for the novice. Appears as a sliver of light with a slight brightenning at its centre. *Located in the same field as Chi-UMa.* *(March)*

NGC 4565   r.a. 12h 34, dec. +26° 16   mag. 11

Edge-on spiral galaxy in Coma Berenices. The dust lanes are clearly visible in a large telescope. Looks like a needle with a central bulge. This has to be one of the finest NGC numbers in the Coma.

Note our 200 mm telephoto shot of the Coma star cluster covering over 5 degrees of the sky. We have circled NGC 4565 for you. *(April)*

o M3

COMA BERNICES

4565 o

Spiral Galaxy easy to locate by beginners NGC 3877

Supernova in a remote galaxy NGC 3953

**Two galaxies in line, one close and the other distant
NGC 4485, 4490**

Edge-on Spiral Galaxy NGC 4565

Coma Berenices showing NGC 4565 taken with 200 mm telephoto lens

THE CONSTELLATIONS

LATIN NAMES WITH PRONUNCIATIONS AND ABBREVIATIONS

Andromeda, ăn-drŏm′ē-da	And	Andr
Antlia, ănt′lĭ-a	Ant	Antl
Apus, ā′pŭs	Aps	Apus
Aquarius, a-kwâr′ĭ-ŭs	Aqr	Aqar
Aquila, ăk′wĭ-la	Aql	Aqil
Ara, ā′ra	Ara	Arae
Aries, ā′rĭ-ēz	Ari	Arie
Auriga, ô-rī′ga	Aur	Auri
Boötes, bō-ō′tēz	Boo	Boot
Caelum, sē′lŭm	Cae	Cael
Camelopardalis, ka-měl′ō-pär′da-lĭs	Cam	Caml
Cancer, kăn′sěr	Cnc	Canc
Canes Venatici, kā′nēz vē-năt′ĭ-sī	CVn	CVen
Canis Major, kā′nĭs mā′jěr	CMa	CMaj
Canis Minor, kā′nĭs′ mĭ′něr	CMi	CMin
Capricornus, kăp′rĭ-kôr′nŭs	Cap	Capr
Carina, ka-rī′na	Car	Cari
Cassiopeia, kăs′ĭ-ō-pē′ya′	Cas	Cas
Centaurus, sěn-tô′rŭs	Cen	Cent
Cepheus, sē′fūs	Cep	Ceph
Cetus, sē′tŭs	Cet	Ceti
Chamaeleon, ka-mē′lē-ŭn	Cha	Cham
Circinus, sûr′sĭ-nŭs	Cir	Circ
Columba, kō-lŭm′ba	Col	Colm
Coma Berenices, kō′ma běr′ē-nī′sēz	Com	Coma
Corona, Australis, kō-rō′na ôs-trā′lĭs	CrA	CorA
Corona Borealis, ka-rō na bō′rē-ā′lĭs	CrB	CorB
Corvus, kôr′vŭs	Crv	Corv
Crater, krā′těr	Crt	Crat
Crux, krŭks	Cru	Cruc
Cygnus, sĭg′nŭs	Cyg	Cygn
Delphinus, děl-fī′nŭs	Del	Dlph
Dorado, dō-rä′dō	Dor	Dora
Draco, drā′kō	Dra	Drac
Equuleus, ē-kwoo′lē-ŭs	Equ	Equl
Eridanus, ē-rĭd′a-nŭs	Eri	Erid
Fornax, fôr′năks	For	Forn
Gemini, jěm′ĭ-ni	Gem	Gemi
Grus, grŭs	Gru	Grus
Hercules, hûr′kū′lēz	Her	Herc
Horologium, hŏr′ō-lō′jĭ-ŭm	Hor	Horo
Hydra, hī′dra	Hya	Hyda
Hydrus, hī′drŭs	Hyi	Hydi
Indus, ĭn′dŭs	Ind	Indi
Lacerta, la-sûr′ta	Lac	Lacr
Leo, lē′ō	Leo	Leon
Leo Minor, lē′ō mī′něr	LMi	LMin
Lepus, lē′pŭs	Lep	Leps
Libra, lī′bra	Lib	Libr
Lupus, lū′pŭs	Lup	Lupi
Lynx, lĭngks	Lyn	Lync
Lyra, lī′ra	Lyr	Lyra
Mensa, měn′sa	Men	Mens
Microscopium, mī′krō-skō′pĭ-ŭm	Mic	Micr
Monoceros, m-ōnŏs′ěr-ŏs	Mon	Mono
Musca, mŭs′ka	Mus	Musc
Norma, nôr′ma	Nor	Norm
Octans, ŏk′tănz	Oct	Octn
Ophiuchus, ŏf′ĭ-ūkŭs	Oph	Ophi
Orion, ō-rī′ŏn	Ori	Orio
Pavo, Pā′vō	Pav	Pavo
Pegasus, pěg′a-sŭs	Peg	Pegs
Perseus, pûr′sūs	Per	Pers
Phoenix, fē′nĭks	Phe	Phoe
Pictor, pĭk′těr	Pic	Pict
Pisces, pĭs′ēz	Psc	Pisc
Piscis Austrinus, pĭs′ĭs ôs-trī′nŭs	PsA	PscA
Puppis, pŭp′ĭs	Pup	Pupp
Pyxis, pĭk′sĭs	Pyx	Pyxi
Reticulum, rē-tĭk′ū-lŭm	Ret	Reti
Sagitta, sa-jĭt′a	Sge	Sgte
Sagittarius, săj′ĭ-tā′rĭ-ŭs	Sgr	Sgtr
Scorpius, skôr′pĭ-ŭs	Sco	Scor
Sculptor, skŭlp′těr	Scl	Scul
Scutum, skū′tŭm	Sct	Scut
Serpens, sûr′pěnz	Ser	Serp
Sextans, sěks′tănz	Sex	Sext
Taurus, tô′rŭs	Tau	Taur
Telescopium, těl′ē-skō′pĭ-ŭm	Tel	Tele
Triangulum, trī-ăng′gū-lŭm	Tri	Tria
Triangulum Australe, trī-ăng′gū-lŭm ôs-trā′lē	Tra	TrAu
Tucana, tū-kā′na	Tuc	Tucn
Ursa Major, ûr′sa mā′jěr	UMa	UMaj
Ursa Minor, ûr′sa mi′něr	UMi	UMin
Vela, vē′la	Vel	Velr
Virgo, vûr′gō	Vir	Virg
Volans, vō′lănz	Vol	Voln
Vulpecula, vŭl-pěk′ū-la	Vul	Vulp

ā fāte; ā chāotic; ă tăp; ă finăl; à àsk; a idea; â câre; ä älms; au aught; ē bē; e crēate; ĕ ĕnd; ĕ angĕl; ē makĕr; ī time; ĭ bĭt; i animal; ō nōte; ō anatōmy; ŏ hŏt; ŏ ŏccur; ô ôrb; ōō mōōn; oo book; ou out; ū tūbe; ū unite; ŭ sŭn; ŭ sŭbmit; û hûrl.

February 9 pm; **January 11 pm**; December 1 am; November 3 am

Canis Major

*	ζ	Zeta-CMa, bluish	6h 20	-30° 03	3.0
+	β	Beta-CMa, bluish	6h 22	-17° 56	2.0v
★	α	Alpha-CMa, Sirius, white	6h 44	-16° 42	-1.5
		M 41, NGC 2287	6h 46	-20° 43	6
★	ε	Epsilon-CMa, Adhara, bluish	6h 58	-28° 57	1.5
*	σ	Sigma-CMa, bluish	7h 02	-23° 48	3.0
+	δ	Delta-CMa, yellowish	7h 08	-26° 22	1.8
+	η	Eta-CMa, bluish	7h 23	-29° 15	2.5

Canis Minor

*	β	Beta-CMi, bluish	7h 26	+08° 20	2.9
★	α	Alpha-CMi, Procyon, yellowish	7h 38	+05° 17	0.4

Gemini

		M 35, NGC 2168	6h 08	+24° 21	6
*	η	Eta-Gem, red	6h 14	+22° 31	3.3v
*	μ	Mu-Gem, red	6h 22	+22° 32	2.9v
+	γ	Gamma-Gem, white	6h 37	+16° 25	1.9
*	ε	Epsilon-Gem, yellow	6h 43	+25° 09	3.0
*	ζ	Zeta-Gem, yellowish	6h 44	+12° 55	3.4
+	α	Alpha-Gem, Castor, white	7h 33	+31° 56	2.0
★	β	Beta-Gem, Pollux, orange	7h 44	+28° 05	1.2

Monoceros

	M 50, NGC 2323	7h 02	-08° 19	7

Puppis

*	ν	Nu-Pup, bluish	6h 37	-43° 11	3.2
*	τ	Tau-Pup, orange	6h 50	-50° 36	2.9
*		L-Pup, red	7h 13	-44° 37	3.4
*	π	Pi-Pup, orange	7h 17	-37° 04	2.7
*	σ	Sigma-Pup, orange	7h 29	-43° 15	3.2
		M 47, NGC 2422	7h 36	-14° 27	5
		M 46, NGC 2437	7h 41	-14° 46	7
		M 93, NGC 2447	7h 44	-23° 49	6
*	ξ	Xi-Pup, yellow	7h 48	-24° 50	3.3
+	ζ	Zeta-Pup, blue	8h 03	-39° 57	2.2
*	ρ	Rho-Pup, yellowish	8h 07	-24° 15	2.8v

Camelopardalis

Carina

★	α	Alpha-Car, Canopus, yellowish	6h 24	-52° 41	-0.7
*	χ	Chi-Car, bluish	7h 56	-52° 56	3.5
+	ε	Epsilon-Car, orange	8h 22	-59° 26	1.9
*		a-Car, bluish	9h 11	-58° 52	3.4
+	β	Beta-Car, white	9h 13	-69° 38	1.7
+	ι	Iota-Car, white	9h 17	-59° 11	2.3
*	ι	Iota-Car, yellow	9h 45	-62° 26	4.1v
*	υ	Upsilon-Car, white	9h 47	-64° 59	3.0
*	ω	Omega-Car, bluish	10h 13	-69° 56	3.3
*		Q-Car, orange	10h 16	-61° 14	3.4v

January 11 pm (Continued)

Carina (Continued)
*	ρ	Rho-Car, bluish	10h 31	-61° 35	3.3v
*	θ	Theta-Car, bluish	10h 42	-64° 17	2.7

Pictor
*	α	Alpha-Pic, white	6h 48	-61° 55	3.3

March 9 pm; **February 11 pm;** January 1 am; December 3 am

Cancer
M 44, NGC 2632, Praesepe	8h 39	+ 20° 04	4
M 67, NGC 2682	8h 50	+ 11° 54	7

Hydra
	M 48, NGC 2548		8h 13	-05° 43	6
*	ε	Epsilon-Hya, yellow	8h 46	+ 06° 30	3.4
*	ζ	Zeta-Hya, orange	8h 54	-06° 02	3.1
+	α	Alpha-Hya, orange	9h 27	-08° 35	2.0
*	ν	Nu-Hya, orange	10h 49	-16° 05	3.1

Lynx
*	α	Alpha-Lyn, red	9h 20	+ 34° 29	3.2

Pyxis

Volans

April 10 pm; **March 11 pm;** February 1 am; January 3 am

Ursa Major
*	o	Omicron-UMa, yellow	8h 29	+ 60° 47	3.4
*	ι	Iota-UMa, white	8h 58	+ 48° 07	3.1
*	θ	Theta-UMa, yellowish	9h 32	+ 51° 46	3.1
	M 81, NGC 3031		9h 54	+ 69° 09	7
	M 82, NGC 3034		9h 54	+ 69° 47	9
*	λ	Lambda-UMa, white	10h 16	+ 43° 01	3.5
*	μ	Mu-UMa, red	10h 21	+ 41° 36	3.1
+	β	Beta-UMa, Merak, white	11h 00	+ 56° 30	2.4
+	α	Alpha-UMa, Dubhe, orange	11h 03	+ 61° 56	1.8
	M 108, NGC 3556		11h 09	+ 55° 57	11
*	ψ	Psi-UMa, orange	11h 09	+ 44° 36	3.0
	M 97, NGC 3587, Owl		11h 14	+ 55° 08	11
	NGC 3877		11h 41	+ 47° 50	12
	NGC 3953		11h 51	+ 52° 37	12
+	γ	Gamma-UMa, Phecda, white	11h 53	+ 53° 49	2.4
	M 109, NGC 3992		11h 55	+ 53° 39	11
*	δ	Delta-UMa, white	12h 14	+ 57° 09	3.3
+	ε	Epsilon-UMa, Alioth, white	12h 53	+ 56° 04	1.8v
+	ζ	Zeta-UMa, Mizar, white	13h 23	+ 55° 02	2.3
+	η	Eta-UMa, Alkaid, bluish	13h 47	+ 49° 25	1.9
	M 101, NGC 5457		14h 03	+ 54° 27	8

Leo
*	ε	Epsilon-Leo, yellow	9h 45	+ 23° 51	3.0
★	α	Alpha-Leo, Regulus, bluish	10h 07	+ 12° 04	1.4
*	ζ	Zeta-Leo, yellowish	10h 16	+ 23° 31	3.5

March 11 pm (Continued)
Leo (Continued)

+	γ	Gamma-Leo, orange	10h 19	+ 19° 57	2.0
		M 95, NGC 3351	10h 43	+ 11° 49	10
		M 105, NGC 3379	10h 45	+ 12° 51	11
		M 96, NGC 3368	10h 46	+ 11° 56	9
*	δ	Delta-Leo, white	11h 13	+ 20° 38	2.6
*	θ	Theta-Leo, white	11h 13	+ 15° 33	3.3
		M 65, NGC 3623	11h 18	+ 13° 13	10
		M 66, NGC 3627	11h 19	+ 13° 07	9
+	β	Beta-Leo, Denebola, white	11h 48	+ 14° 41	2.1

Leo Minor

Chamaeleon

Antlia

Crater

Vela

+	γ	Gamma-Vel	8h 09	-47° 18	1.9
+	δ	Delta-Vel, white	8h 44	-54° 38	1.9
+	λ	Lambda-Vel, orange	9h 07	-43° 21	2.2
+	κ	Kappa-Vel, bluish	9h 22	-54° 56	2.5
*	ν	Nu-Vel, orange	9h 31	-56° 57	3.2
*	μ	Mu-Vel, yellow	10h 46	-49° 19	2.7

Sextans

May 10 pm; **April midnight;** March 1 am; February 3 am
Virgo

		M 61, NGC 4303	12h 21	+ 04° 36	10
		M 84, NGC 4374	12h 24	+ 13° 00	10
		M 86, NGC 4406	12h 25	+ 13° 03	10
		M 49, NGC 4472	12h 29	+ 08° 07	9
		M 87, NGC 4486	12h 30	+ 12° 30	9
		M 89, NGC 4552	12h 35	+ 12° 40	10
		M 90, NGC 4569	12h 36	+ 13° 16	10
		M 104, NGC 4594, Sombrero	12h 37	-11° 21	8
		M 58, NGC 4579	12h 37	+ 11° 56	10
		M 59, NGC 4621	12h 41	+ 11° 47	10
*	γ	Gamma-Vir, yellowish	12h 41	-01° 20	2.8
		M 60, NGC 4649	12h 43	+ 11° 41	9
*	ε	Epsilon-Vir, yellow	13h 01	+ 11° 05	2.8
★	α	Alpha-Vir, Spica, bluish	13h 24	-11° 03	1.0v
*	ζ	Zeta-Vir, white	13h 34	-00° 30	3.4

Coma Berenices

M 98, NGC 4192	12h 13	+ 15° 01	10
M 99, NGC 4254	12h 18	+ 14° 32	10
M 100, NGC 4321	12h 22	+ 15° 56	10
M 85, NGC 4382	12h 24	+ 18° 18	10
NGC 4414, **Super-Nova**	12h 25	+ 31° 22	
M 88, NGC 4501	12h 31	+ 14° 32	10
NGC 4565	12h 34	+ 26° 16	11

April midnight (Continued)

Coma Berenices (Continued)

M 64, NGC 4826, Black-eye	12h 56	+ 21° 48	9
M 53, NGC 5024	13h 12	+ 18° 17	8

Canes Venatici

	M 106, NGC 4258	12h 17	+ 47° 35	10
	NGC 4485/4490	12h 28	+ 41° 58	13
	M 94, NGC 4736	12h 50	+ 41° 14	8
α	Alpha-CVn, bluish	12h 55	+ 38° 26	2.9v
	M 63, NGC 5055	13h 15	+ 42° 08	9
	M 51, NGC 5194, Whirlpool	13h 29	+ 47° 18	8
	M 3, NGC 5272	13h 41	+ 28° 29	6

Hydra

	M 68, NGC 4590	12h 38	-26° 38	8
* γ	Gamma-Hya, yellow	13h 18	-23° 04	3.0
	M 83, NGC 5236	13h 36	-29° 46	8
* π	Pi-Hya, orange	14h 05	-26° 35	3.3

Corvus

* ε	Epsilon-Crv, orange	12h 09	-22° 30	3.0
* γ	Gamma-Crv, bluish	12h 15	-17° 25	2.6
* δ	Delta-Crv, bluish	12h 29	-16° 24	3.0
* β	Beta-Crv, yellow	12h 33	-23° 17	2.7

Crux

* δ	Delta-Cru, bluish	12h 14	-58° 38	2.8v
★ α	Alpha-Cru, Acrux, bluish	12h 25	-62° 59	1.4
+ γ	Gamma-Cru, red	12h 30	-57° 00	1.7
★ β	Beta-Cru, Beta Crucis, bluish	12h 47	-59° 35	1.3v

Musca

* α	Alpha-Mus, bluish	12h 36	-69° 01	2.7v
* β	Beta-Mus, bluish	12h 45	-68° 00	3.1

June 10 pm; **May midnight;** April 2 am; March 3 am

Serpens

	M 5, NGC 5904	15h 18	+ 02° 11	6
* α	Alpha-Ser, orange	15h 43	+ 06° 29	2.7

Ursa Minor

+ α	Alpha-UMi, Polaris, yellowish	2h 13	+ 89° 11	2.0v
+ β	Beta-UMi, Kochab, orange	14h 51	+ 74° 14	2.1
* γ	Gamma-UMi, white	15h 21	+ 71° 54	3.0

Bootes

* η	Eta-Boo, yellow	13h 54	+ 18° 30	2.7
★ α	Alpha-Boo, Arcturus, orange	14h 15	+ 19° 17	-0.1
* γ	Gamma-Boo, white	14h 31	+ 38° 24	3.1
+ ε	Epsilon-Boo, orange	14h 44	+ 27° 09	2.4
* β	Beta-Boo, yellow	15h 01	+ 40° 28	3.5
* δ	Delta-Boo, yellow	15h 15	+ 33° 24	3.5

Corona Borealis

+ α	Alpha-CrB, white	15h 34	+ 26° 47	2.2v

May midnight (Continued)

Libra
*	α	Alpha-Lib, white	14h 50	-15° 54	2.8
*	σ	Sigma-Lib, red	15h 03	-25° 12	3.3
*	β	Beta-Lib, bluish	15h 16	-09° 18	2.6

Centaurus
*	λ	Lambda-Cen, bluish	11h 35	-62° 54	3.2
*	δ	Delta-Cen, bluish	12h 07	-50° 36	2.6v
+	γ	Gamma-Cen, white	12h 40	-48° 51	2.1
*	ι	Iota-Cen, white	13h 20	-36° 36	2.8
+	ε	Epsilon-Cen, bluish	13h 39	-53° 22	2.3v
*	ν	Nu-Cen, bluish	13h 48	-41° 35	3.4
*	μ	Mu-Cen, bluish	13h 48	-42° 23	3.1v
*	ζ	Zeta-Cen, bluish	13h 54	-47° 12	2.6
★	β	Beta-Cen, Hadar, bluish	14h 02	-60° 16	0.6v
+	θ	Theta-Cen, orange	14h 05	-36° 17	2.0
+	η	Eta-Cen, bluish	14h 34	-42° 01	2.4v
★	α	Alpha-Cen, Rigil Kentaurus, yellow	14h 38	-60° 46	0.0
*	κ	Kappa-Cen, bluish	14h 58	-42° 01	3.2

Lupus
+	α	Alpha-Lup, bluish	14h 41	-47° 19	2.3v
*	β	Beta-Lup, bluish	14h 57	-43° 03	2.7
*	ζ	Zeta-Lup, orange	15h 11	-52° 01	3.4
*	δ	Delta-Lup, bluish	15h 20	-40° 34	3.2v
*	γ	Gamma-Lup, bluish	15h 34	-41° 06	2.8
*	η	Eta-Lup, bluish	15h 59	-38° 21	3.4

Circinus
*	α	Alpha-Cir, white	14h 41	-64° 53	3.2

.

July 10 pm; June midnight; May 2 am; April 4 am

Scorpius
*	π	Pi-Sco, bluish	15h 58	-26° 04	2.9
+	δ	Delta-Sco, bluish	15h 59	-22° 34	2.3
*	β	Beta-Sco, bluish	16h 04	-19° 45	2.7
*	σ	Sigma-Sco, bluish	16h 20	-25° 32	2.9v
	M 80, NGC 6093		16h 16	-22° 56	7
	M 4, NGC 6121		16h 22	-26° 27	6
★	α	Alpha-Sco, Antares, red	16h 28	-26° 23	0.9v
*	τ	Tau-Sco, bluish	16h 35	-28° 10	2.9
+	ε	Epsilon-Sco, orange	16h 49	-34° 16	2.3
*	μ	Mu-Sco, bluish	16h 51	-38° 01	3.0v
	M 62, NGC 6266		17h 00	-30° 05	7
*	η	Eta-Sco, yellowish	17h 11	-43° 13	3.3
*	υ	Upsilon-Sco, bluish	17h 29	-37° 16	2.7
+	λ	Lambda-Sco, Shaula, bluish	17h 32	-37° 05	1.6v
+	θ	Theta-Sco, yellowish	17h 36	-42° 59	1.9
	M 6, NGC 6405		17h 39	-32° 11	6
+	κ	Kappa-Sco, bluish	17h 41	-39° 01	2.4
*	ι	Iota-Sco, yellowish	17h 46	-40° 06	3.0
*		G-Sco, orange	17h 48	-37° 02	3.2
	M 7, NGC 6475		17h 53	-34° 48	5

June midnight (Continued)

Hercules

*	β	Beta-Her, yellow	16h 29	+ 21° 32	2.8
		M 13, NGC 6205, Great cl.	16h 41	+ 36° 30	6
*	ζ	Zeta-Her, yellow	16h 41	+ 31° 38	2.8
*	η	Eta-Her, yellow	16h 42	+ 38° 58	3.5
*	π	Pi-Her, orange	17h 14	+ 36° 49	3.1
*	δ	Delta-Her, white	17h 14	+ 24° 51	3.1
*	α	Alpha-Her, red	17h 14	+ 14° 24	3.1v
		M 92, NGC 6341	17h 17	+ 43° 10	6
*	μ	Mu-Her, yellow	17h 46	+ 27° 45	3.4

Ophiuchus

*	δ	Delta-Oph, red	16h 13	-03° 37	2.7
*	ε	Epsilon-Oph, yellow	16h 17	-04° 39	3.2
		M 107, NGC 6171	16h 30	-12° 57	10
*	ζ	Zeta-Oph, blue	16h 36	-10° 31	2.6
		M 12, NGC 6218	16h 46	-01° 55	7
		M 10, NGC 6254	16h 56	-04° 05	6
*	κ	Kappa-Oph, orange	16h 57	+ 09° 25	3.2
		M 19, NGC 6273	17h 01	-26° 14	7
+	η	Eta-Oph, white	17h 09	-15° 42	2.4
		M 9, NGC 6333	17h 18	-18° 30	8
*	θ	Theta-Oph, bluish	17h 21	-24° 59	3.3v
+	α	Alpha-Oph, white	17h 34	+ 12° 35	2.1
		M 14, NGC 6402	17h 37	-03° 14	8
*	β	Beta-Oph, orange	17h 43	+ 04° 35	2.8
*	ν	Nu-Oph, yellow	17h 58	-09° 47	3.3

Draco

		M 102, NGC 5866	15h 05	+ 55° 57	8
*	ι	Iota-Dra, orange	15h 25	+ 59° 02	3.3
*	η	Eta-Dra, yellow	16h 24	+ 61° 33	2.7
*	ζ	Zeta-Dra, bluish	17h 09	+ 65° 44	3.2
*	δ	Delta-Dra, yellow	19h 13	+ 67° 38	3.1
*	β	Beta-Dra, yellow	17h 30	+ 52° 20	2.8
+	γ	Gamma-Dra, orange	17h 56	+ 51° 29	2.2

Ara

*	ζ	Zeta-Ara, orange	16h 59	-55° 57	3.1
*	β	Beta-Ara, orange	17h 24	-55° 31	2.9
*	γ	Gamma-Ara, bluish	17h 24	-56° 22	3.3
*	α	Alpha-Ara, bluish	17h 30	-49° 52	3.0

Triangulum Australe

*	γ	Gamma-TrA, white	15h 17	-68° 36	2.9
*	β	Beta-TrA, yellowish	15h 53	-63° 22	2.8
+	α	Alpha-TrA, orange	16h 47	-68° 60	1.9

Apus

Norma

Sagittarius

	M 23, NGC 6494		17h 56	-19° 00	6
	M 20, NGC 6514, Trifid		18h 01	-23° 02	
	M 8, NGC 6523, Lagoon		18h 02	-24° 23	
	M 21, NGC 6531		18h 03	-22° 30	7
*	γ	Gamma-Sgr, orange	18h 05	-30° 26	3.0
*	η	Eta-Sgr, red	18h 16	-36° 47	3.1
	M 24, NGC 6603		18h 17	-18° 27	6
	M 18, NGC 6613		18h 19	-17° 09	7
	M 17, NGC 6618, Omega		18h 20	-16° 12	7
*	δ	Delta-Sgr, orange	18h 20	-29° 50	2.7
	M 28, NGC 6626		18h 23	-24° 52	7
+	ε	Epsilon-Sgr, bluish	18h 23	-34° 24	1.8
*	λ	Lambda-Sgr, orange	18h 27	-25° 27	2.8
	M 69, NGC 6637		18h 30	-32° 23	8
	M 25, NGC 4725		18h 31	-19° 16	6
	M 22, NGC 6656		18h 35	-23° 55	5
	M 70, NGC 6681		18h 42	-32° 18	8
*	φ	Phi-Sgr, bluish	18h 44	-27° 01	3.2
+	σ	Sigma-Sgr, bluish	18h 54	-26° 19	2.1
	M 54, NGC 6715		18h 54	-30° 30	8
*	ζ	Zeta-Sgr, orange	18h 56	-21° 07	3.5
*	ζ	Zeta-Sgr, white	19h 01	-29° 54	2.6
*	τ	Tau-Sgr, orange	19h 06	-27° 42	3.3
*	π	Pi-Sgr, yellowish	19h 09	-21° 03	2.9
	M 55, NGC 6809		19h 39	-31° 00	6
	M 75, NGC 6864		20h 05	-21° 59	8

Lyra

★	α	Alpha-Lyr, Vega, white	18h 36	+ 38° 46	0.0
*	β	Beta-Lyr, bluish	18h 49	+ 33° 21	3.4v
	M 57, NGC 6720, Ring		18h 53	+ 33° 01	9
*	γ	Gamma-Lyr, bluish	18h 58	+ 32° 40	3.3
	M 56, NGC 6779		19h 16	+ 30° 08	8

Sagitta

M 71, NGC 6838	19h 53	+ 18° 44	7

Scutum

M 26, NGC 6694	18h 44	-09° 25	9
M 11, NGC 6705	18h 50	-06° 18	7

Vulpecula

M 27, NGC 6853, dumbbell	19h 59	+ 22° 40	8

Serpens

	M 16, NGC 6611		18h 18	-13° 48	7
*	η	Eta-Ser, orange	18h 20	-02° 54	3.2

Corona Australis

Telescopium

September 10 pm; **August midnight;** July 2 am; June 4 am

Cygnus

*	β	Beta-Cyg, orange	19h 30	+ 27° 55	3.1
*	δ	Delta-Cyg, bluish	19h 44	+ 45° 05	2.9
+	γ	Gamma-Cyg, yellowish	20h 22	+ 40° 11	2.2
		M 29, NGC 6913	20h 23	+ 38° 27	8
★	α	Alpha-Cyg, Deneb, white	20h 41	+ 45° 12	1.3
+	ε	Epsilon-Cyg, orange	20h 45	+ 33° 53	2.5
		Veil, NGC 6960	20h 45	+ 30° 38	
		Veil, NGC 6992, 6995	20h 55	+ 31° 30	
*	ζ	Zeta-Cyg, yellow	21h 12	+ 30° 08	3.2
		M 39, NGC 7092	21h 32	+ 48° 21	6

Aquila

*	ζ	Zeta-Aql, white	19h 05	+ 13° 50	3.0
*	λ	Lambda-Aql, bluish	19h 05	-04° 55	3.4
*	δ	Delta-Aql, yellowish	19h 25	+ 03° 04	3.4
*	γ	Gamma-Aql, orange	19h 45	+ 10° 33	2.7
★	α	Alpha-Aql, Altair, white	19h 50	+ 08° 49	0.8
*	θ	Theta-Aql, bluish	20h 10	-00° 52	3.2

Pegasus

		M 15, NGC 7078	21h 29	+ 12° 05	6
+	ε	Epsilon-Peg, orange	21h 43	+ 09° 48	2.4
*	ζ	Zeta-Peg, bluish	22h 41	+ 10° 44	3.4
*	η	Eta-Peg, yellow	22h 42	+ 30° 07	3.0
+	β	Beta-Peg, red	23h 03	+ 27° 58	2.5v
+	α	Alpha-Peg, bluish	23h 04	+ 15° 05	2.5
*	γ	Gamma-Peg, bluish	0h 12	+ 15° 04	2.8v

Cepheus

*	η	Eta-Cep, orange	20h 45	+ 61° 45	3.4
+	α	Alpha-Cep, white	21h 18	+ 62° 31	2.4
*	β	Beta-Cep, bluish	21h 28	+ 70° 28	3.2v
*	ζ	Zeta-Cep, orange	22h 10	+ 58° 06	3.4
*	δ	Delta-Cep, yellowish	22h 29	+ 58° 19	4.0v
*	γ	Gamma-Cep, orange	23h 39	+ 77° 30	3.2

Capricornus

*	β	Beta-Cap	20h 20	-14° 51	3.1
		M 30, NGC 7099	21h 39	-23° 15	8
*	δ	Delta-Cap, white	21h 46	-16° 13	2.9v

Aquarius

		M 72, NGC 6981	20h 53	-12° 39	9
		M 73, NGC 6994	20h 58	-12° 44	
*	β	Beta-Aqr, yellow	21h 31	-05° 40	2.9
		M 2, NGC 7089	21h 32	-00° 54	6
*	α	Alpha-Aqr, yellow	22h 05	-00° 25	2.9
*	δ	Delta-Aqr, white	22h 54	-15° 56	3.3

Delphinus

Equuleus

August midnight (Continued)

Pavo
+	α	Alpha-Pav, bluish	20h 24	-56° 48	2.0
*	β	Beta-Pav, white	20h 43	-66° 17	3.5

Indus
*	α	Alpha-Ind, orange	20h 36	-47° 21	3.1

Microscopium

October 10 pm; **September midnight;** August 2 am; July 4 am

Cassiopeia
		M 52, NGC 7654	23h 23	+ 61° 29	7
+	β	Beta-Cas, yellowish	0h 08	+ 59° 02	2.3v
+	α	Alpha-Cas, orange	0h 39	+ 56° 25	2.2
*	η	Eta-Cas, yellow	0h 48	+ 57° 42	3.5
+	γ	Gamma-Cas, bluish	0h 56	+ 60° 36	2.5v
*	δ	Delta-Cas, white	1h 24	+ 60° 08	2.7
		M 103, NGC 581	1h 32	+ 60° 35	7
*	ϵ	Epsilon-Cas, bluish	1h 53	+ 63° 34	3.4

Lacerta

Piscis Austrinus
★	α	Alpha-PsA, Fomalhaut, white	22h 57	-29° 44	1.2

Grus
*	γ	Gamma-Gru, bluish	21h 53	-37° 27	3.0
+	α	Alpha-Gru, bluish	22h 07	-47° 04	1.8
+	β	Beta-Gru, red	22h 42	-46° 59	2.2v

Tucana
*	α	Alpha-Tuc, orange	22h 17	-60° 21	2.9

Octans

November 9 pm; **October midnight;** September 2 am; August 4 am

Andromeda
+	α	Alpha-And, bluish	0h 07	+ 28° 58	2.1
*	δ	Delta-And, orange	0h 38	+ 30° 45	3.3
		M 31, NGC 224, Great galaxy	0h 42	+ 41° 09	4
		M 32, NGC 221	0h 42	+ 40° 45	9
+	β	Beta-And, Mirach, red	1h 09	+ 35° 31	2.0
+	γ	Gamma-And, orange	2h 03	+ 42° 14	2.2

Triangulum
		M 33, NGC 598	1h 33	+ 30° 33	6
	α	Alpha-Tri, yellowish	1h 52	+ 29° 29	3.4
	β	Beta-Tri, white	2h 08	+ 34° 54	3.0

Pisces
		M 74, NGC 628	1h 36	+ 15° 41	10

October midnight (Continued)
Perseus

		M 76, NGC 650	1h 41	+ 51° 28	11
		NGC 869, 884, Double cluster	2h 18	+ 57° 04	10
		M 34, NGC 1039	2h 41	+ 42° 43	6
*	γ	Gamma-Per, yellow	3h 03	+ 53° 25	2.9
*	ρ	Rho-Per, red	3h 04	+ 38° 45	3.5v
+	β	Beta-Per, Algol, bluish	3h 07	+ 40° 52	2.1v
+	α	Alpha-Per, yellowish	3h 23	+ 49° 47	1.8
*	δ	Delta-Per, bluish	3h 42	+ 47° 44	3.0
*	ζ	Zeta-Per, bluish	3h 53	+ 31° 50	2.8
*	ε	Epsilon-Per, bluish	3h 57	+ 39° 57	2.9

Hydrus

*	β	Beta-Hyi, yellow	0h 25	-77° 22	2.8
*	α	Alpha-Hyi, yellowish	1h 58	-61° 40	2.8
*	γ	Gamma-Hyi, red	3h 48	-74° 18	3.3

Phoenix

+	α	Alpha-Phe, orange	0h 25	-42° 25	2.4
*	β	Beta-Phe, yellow	1h 05	-46° 50	3.3
*	γ	Gamma-Phe, orange	1h 28	-43° 25	3.4

Sculptor

December 9 pm; **November 11 pm;** October 2 am; September 4 am

Aries

*	β	Beta-Ari, white	1h 54	+ 20° 43	2.7
+	α	Alpha-Ari, orange	2h 06	+ 23° 22	2.0

Cetus

+	β	Beta-Cet, orange	0h 43	-18° 06	2.0
*	η	Eta-Cet, orange	1h 08	-10° 17	3.4
*	τ	Tau-Cet, yellow	1h 43	-16° 03	3.5
*	o	Omicron-Cet, Mira, red	2h 18	-03° 04	2.0v
		M 77, NGC 1068	2h 42	-00° 04	9
*	γ	Gamma-Cet, white	2h 42	-03° 10	3.5
+	α	Alpha-Cet, red	3h 01	+ 04° 00	2.5

Eridanus

★	α	Alpha-Eri, Achernar, bluish	1h 37	-57° 20	0.5
*	θ	Theta-Eri, white	2h 57	-40° 23	2.9
*	γ	Gamma-Eri, red	3h 57	-13° 34	3.0
*	β	Beta-Eri, white	5h 07	-05° 06	2.8

Fornax

Horologium

Orion

*	π	Pi-Ori, yellowish	4h 48	+06° 56	3.2
★	β	Beta-Ori, Rigel, bluish	5h 14	-08° 13	0.2v
+	γ	Gamma-Ori, Bellatrix, bluish	5h 24	+06° 20	1.6
*	η	Eta-Ori, bluish	5h 24	-02° 24	3.3v
+	δ	Delta-Ori, blue	5h 31	-00° 19	2.2v
		M 42, NGC 1976, Great neb.	5h 34	-05° 24	
*	λ	Lambda-Ori, blue	5h 34	+09° 55	3.4
+	ε	Epsilon-Ori, bluish	5h 35	-01° 13	1.7
		M 43, NGC 1982	5h 35	-05° 18	
*	ι	Iota-Ori, blue	5h 35	-05° 56	2.8
		IC 434, Horsehead	5h 39	-02° 26	
+	ζ	Zeta-Ori, blue	5h 40	-01° 57	1.8
		M 78, NGC 2068	5h 46	+00° 02	
+	κ	Kappa-Ori, bluish	5h 47	-09° 41	2.1
★	α	Alpha-Ori, Betelgeuse, red	5h 54	+07° 24	0.4v

Taurus

		M 45, Pleiades	3h 46	+24° 03	2
*	η	Eta-Tau, bluish	3h 46	+24° 03	2.9
*	ε	Epsilon-Tau, orange	4h 27	+19° 08	3.5
*	θ	Theta-Tau, white	4h 27	+15° 49	3.4
★	α	Alpha-Tau, Aldebaran, orange	4h 35	+16° 28	0.9v
+	β	Beta-Tau, bluish	5h 25	+28° 36	1.6
		M 1, NGC 1952, Crab	5h 33	+22° 01	11
*	ζ	Zeta-Tau, bluish	5h 37	+21° 08	3.1

Auriga

*	ι	Iota-Aur, orange	4h 56	+33° 08	2.7
*	ε	Epsilon-Aur, yellowish	5h 00	+43° 48	3.0v
*	η	Eta-Aur, bluish	5h 05	+41° 13	3.2
★	α	Alpha-Aur, Capella, yellow	5h 15	+45° 59	0.1
		M 38, NGC 1912	5h 27	+35° 48	6
		M 36, NGC 1960	5h 35	+34° 05	6
		M 37, NGC 2099	5h 52	+32° 33	6
+	β	Beta-Aur, white	5h 58	+44° 57	1.9
*	θ	Theta-Aur, bluish	5h 58	+37° 13	2.7v

Lepus

*	ε	Epsilon-Lep, orange	5h 05	-22° 24	3.2
*	μ	Mu-Lep, bluish	5h 12	-16° 13	3.3
*	β	Beta-Lep, yellow	5h 27	-20° 47	2.8
		M 79, NGC 1904	5h 23	-24° 32	7
*	α	Alpha-Lep, yellowish	5h 32	-17° 51	2.6

Dorado

*	α	Alpha-Dor, white	4h 34	-55° 05	3.3

Reticulum

*	α	Alpha-Ret, yellow	4h 14	-62° 32	3.3

Columba

*	α	Alpha-Col, bluish	5h 39	-34° 05	2.6
*	β	Beta-Col, orange	5h 50	-35° 47	3.1

Caelum

SYMBOLS AND ABBREVIATIONS

SUN, MOON AND PLANETS

☉	The Sun	☽	The Moon generally	♃	Jupiter
🌑	New Moon	☿	Mercury	♄	Saturn
🌕	Full Moon	♀	Venus	♅	Uranus
🌓	First Quarter	⊕	Earth	♆	Neptune
🌗	Last Quarter	♂	Mars	♇	Pluto

SIGNS OF THE ZODIAC

♈	Aries..........0°	♌	Leo..........120°	♐	Sagittarius....240°
♉	Taurus........30°	♍	Virgo........150°	♑	Capricornus ..270°
♊	Gemini........60°	♎	Libra.........180°	♒	Aquarius.....300°
♋	Cancer.........90°	♏	Scorpius......210°	♓	Pisces.......330°

THE GREEK ALPHABET

A, α	Alpha	I, ι	Iota	P, ρ	Rho
B, β	Beta	K, κ	Kappa	Σ, σ	Sigma
Γ, γ	Gamma	Λ, λ	Lambda	T, τ	Tau
Δ, δ	Delta	M, μ	Mu	Υ, υ	Upsilon
E, ε	Epsilon	N, ν	Nu	Φ, φ	Phi
Z, ζ	Zeta	Ξ, ξ	Xi	X, χ	Chi
H, η	Eta	O, o	Omicron	Ψ, ψ	Psi
Θ, θ, ϑ	Theta	Π, π	Pi	Ω, ω	Omega

CO-ORDINATE SYSTEMS AND TERMINOLOGY

Astronomical positions are usually measured in a system based on the *celestial poles* and *celestial equator*, the intersections of the earth's rotation axis and equatorial plane, respectively, and the infinite sphere of the sky. *Right ascension* (R.A. or α) is measured in hours (h), minutes (m) and seconds (s) of time, eastward along the celestial equator from the *vernal equinox*. *Declination* (Dec. or δ) is measured in degrees (°), minutes (') and seconds ('') of arc, northward (N or +) or southward (S or −) from the celestial equator toward the N or S celestial pole. One hour of time equals 15 degrees.

Positions can also be measured in a system based on the *ecliptic*, the intersection of the earth's orbit plane and the infinite sphere of the sky. The sun appears to move eastward along the ecliptic during the year. *Longitude* is measured eastward along the ecliptic from the vernal equinox; *latitude* is measured at right angles to the ecliptic, northward or southward toward the N or S ecliptic pole. The *vernal equinox* is one of the two intersections of the ecliptic and the celestial equator; it is the one at which the sun crosses the celestial equator moving from south to north.

Objects are *in conjunction* if they have the same longitude or R.A., and are *in opposition* if they have longitudes or R.A.'s which differ by 180°. If the second object is not specified, it is assumed to be the sun. For instance, if a planet is "in conjunction", it has the same longitude as the sun. At *superior conjunction*, the planet is more distant than the sun; at *inferior conjunction*, it is nearer.

If an object crosses the ecliptic moving northward, it is at the *ascending node* of its orbit; if it crosses the ecliptic moving southward, it is at the *descending node*.

Elongation is the difference in longitude between an object and a second object (usually the sun). At conjunction, the elongation of a planet is thus zero.

MISCELLANEOUS ASTRONOMICAL DATA

UNITS OF LENGTH

1 Angstrom unit	$= 10^{-8}$ cm	1 micrometre, $\mu = 10^{-4}$ cm $= 10^4$A.
1 inch	= exactly 2.54 centimetres	1 cm = 10 mm = 0.39370 ... in
1 yard	= exactly 0.9144 metre	1 m = 10^2 cm = 1.0936 .... yd
1 mile	= exactly 1.609344 kilometres	1 km = 10^5 cm = 0.62137 ... mi

1 astronomical unit $= 1.4960 \times 10^{13}$ cm $= 1.496 \times 10^8$ km $= 9.2956 \times 10^7$ mi
1 light-year $= 9.461 \times 10^{17}$ cm $= 5.88 \times 10^{12}$ mi = 0.3068 parsecs
1 parsec $= 3.086 \times 10^{18}$ cm $= 1.917 \times 10^{13}$ mi = 3.262 l.y.
1 megaparsec $= 10^6$ parsecs

UNITS OF TIME

Sidereal day $= 23h\ 56m\ 04.09s$ of mean solar time
Mean solar day $= 24h\ 03m\ 56.56s$ of mean sidereal time
Synodic month $= 29d\ 12h\ 44m\ 03s = 29\overset{d}{.}5306$ Sidereal month $= 27d\ 07h\ 43m\ 12s$
Tropical year (ordinary) $= 365d\ 05h\ 48m\ 46s = 365\overset{d}{.}2422$ $= 27\overset{d}{.}3216$
Sidereal year $= 365d\ 06h\ 09m\ 10s = 365\overset{d}{.}2564$
Eclipse year $= 346d\ 14h\ 52m\ 52s = 346\overset{d}{.}6200$

THE EARTH

Equatorial radius, a = 6378.164 km = 3963.21 mi: flattening, $c = (a - b)/a = 1/298.25$
Polar radius, b = 6356.779 km = 3949.92 mi
1° of latitude $= 111.133 - 0.559 \cos 2\phi$ km $= 69.055 - 0.347 \cos 2\phi$ mi (at lat. ϕ)
1° of longitude $= 111.413 \cos \phi - 0.094 \cos 3\phi$ km $= 69.229 \cos \phi - 0.0584 \cos 3\phi$ mi
Mass of earth $= 5.976 \times 10^{24}$ kgm $= 13.17 \times 10^{24}$ lb
Velocity of escape from $\oplus = 11.2$ km/sec = 6.94 mi/sec

EARTH'S ORBITAL MOTION

Solar parallax = 8″.794 (adopted)
Constant of aberration = 20″.496 (adopted)
Annual general precession = 50″.26; obliquity of ecliptic = 23° 26′ 35″ (1970)
Orbital velocity = 29.8 km/sec = 18.5 mi/sec
Parabolic velocity at $\oplus$ = 42.3 km/sec = 26.2 mi/sec

SOLAR MOTION

Solar apex, R.A. $18h\ 04m$, Dec. + 30°; solar velocity = 19.75 km/sec = 12.27 mi/sec

THE GALACTIC SYSTEM

North pole of galactic plane R.A. $12h\ 49m$, Dec. + 27.°4 (1950)
Centre of galaxy R.A. $17h\ 42.4m$, Dec. − 28° 55′ (1950) (zero pt. for new gal. coord.)
Distance to centre $\sim$ 10,000 parsecs; diameter $\sim$ 30,000 parsecs
Rotational velocity (at sun) $\sim$ 250 km/sec
Rotational period (at sun) $\sim 2.46 \times 10^8$ years
Mass $\sim 1.4 \times 10^{11}$ solar masses

EXTERNAL GALAXIES

Red Shift $\sim$ + 75 km/sec/megaparsec $\sim$ 14 miles/sec/million l.y.

RADIATION CONSTANTS

Velocity of light, $c = 2.997925 \times 10^{10}$ cm/sec = 186,282.1 mi/sec
Frequency, $\nu = c/\lambda$; ν in Hertz (cycles per sec), c in cm/sec, λ in cm
Solar constant = 1.950 gram calories/square cm/minute $= 1.36 \times 10^6$ cgs units
Light ratio for one magnitude = 2.512 ... ; log ratio = exactly 0.4
Stefan's constant $= 5.66956 \times 10^{-5}$ cgs units

MISCELLANEOUS

Constant of gravitation, $G = 6.6727 \times 10^{-8}$ cgs units
Mass of the electron, $m = 9.1096 \times 10^{-28}$ gm: mass of the proton $= 1.6727 \times 10^{-24}$ gm
Planck's constant, $h = 6.6262 \times 10^{-27}$ erg sec
Absolute temperature $= T°$ K $= T°$ C $+ 273° = 5/9\ (T°$ F $+ 459°)$
1 radian   = 57°.2958 π = 3.141,592,653,6
            = 3437′.75   No. of square degrees in the sky = 41,253
            = 206,265″   1 gram = 0.03527 oz

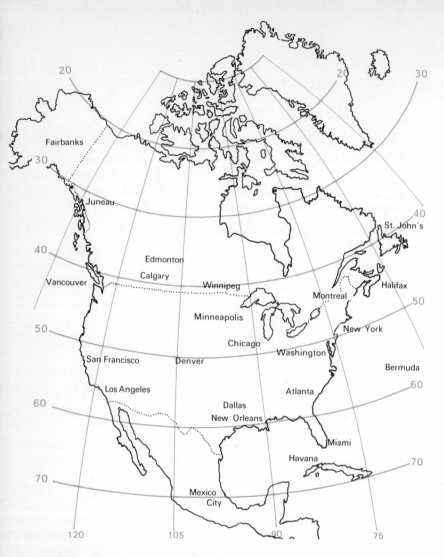

Map of North America showing limiting horizons.

The numbers on the side of the map are the limits of your circumpolar stars when taken as positive and the limits of your southern horizon when taken as negative. All objects with a greater declination than the number for your location will never set. All objects with a lesser declination will never rise.

If you live in Edmonton, the number is 35. Taken as positive, all stars and objects above +35 will never set. Taken as negative all stars and objects below -35 will never rise above the horizon when looking due south.

On the other hand, if you live in Miami, the number is 65. The 'Dipper' will completely set in September, but the 'Southern Cross' will rise above the southern horizon in March.

How to use the star charts

The sky for an observer looking north.

All the stars, constellations and objects appear to rotate counterclockwise about the single pole star known as Polaris. This star does not appear to move more than one degree and is therefore always in the same place.

Circumpolar map, pages 152 and 153.

Look north. Hold the book so that the current month reads upright. This will be how the sky looks at midnight Daylight time or 11 p.m. Standard time. The star completing the Little Dipper is not shown. This was intentional because, for people living in large cities as personal experience in Toronto has shown, 5th magnitude stars are not available for naked-eye observation.

The sky for an observer looking south.

When **looking south** the sky appears to rotate clockwise about one month's division every two hours. That is, the sun, the moon, the planets, the stars, galaxies etc. appear to rise in the east, reach their highest position between Polaris and a point directly south (culminate) and then set in the west.

Southern maps, pages 154 to 159.

If you look at the sky just after sunset during the winter you may be looking up to 2 full months, according to our charts, into the past. By staying up past midnight, you look into the future. After about 1 a.m. in December you will see our January sky charts.

You can see one month in the past by looking toward the west and one month into the future by looking toward the east. By looking farther east or west, it is possible to see additional months, but you will have to tilt the book to see the constellation asterisms.

The **railway track** running across the southern charts is the Ecliptic. This is a narrow band of sky where all the visible planets and the moon travel as the year progresses. These wanderers are not plotted for obvious reasons.

The **stars** have been coded by symbol. There are 22 ★'S WHICH REPRESENT THE BRIGHTEST IN THE SKY AND SHOULD BE KNOWN BY EVERYONE. There are 65 + 's which are the next brightest. The following *'s represent about 200 of the stars which can be readily seen in the city. All asterisms should be identified by the serious amateur. A good way to learn the sky is to plot star charts. We know it works. The various large dots you see represent stars from about 3.5 magnitude through to 5th. The smaller dots go to about 7th magnitude.

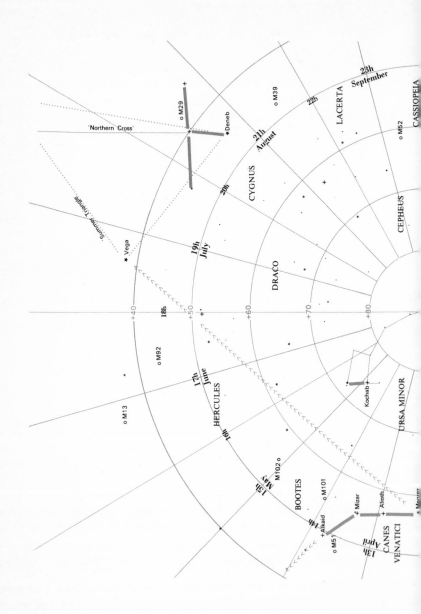

CASSIOPEIA

23h
September

22h

LACERTA

o M39

o M52

CEPHEUS

21h
August

CYGNUS

o M29

+

+ Deneb

'Northern Cross'

20h

+

DRACO

Summer Triangle

★ Vega

19h
July

18h

+40

+50

+60

+70

+80

URSA MINOR

Kochab +

o M92

17h
June

HERCULES

16h

o M13

o M102

15h
May

BOOTES

M102 o

o M101

14h

+ Mizar

+ Alioth

Alkaid +

o M5

CANES
VENATICI

13h
April

Merez

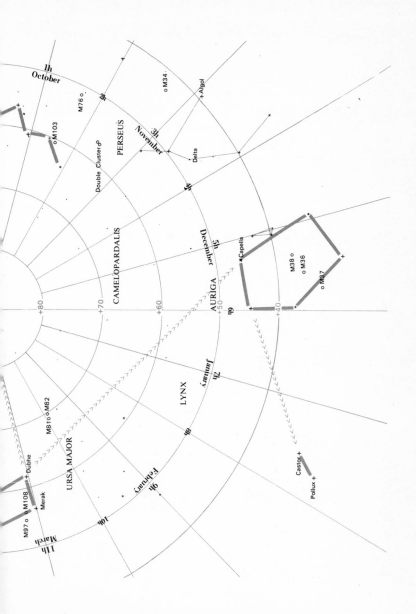

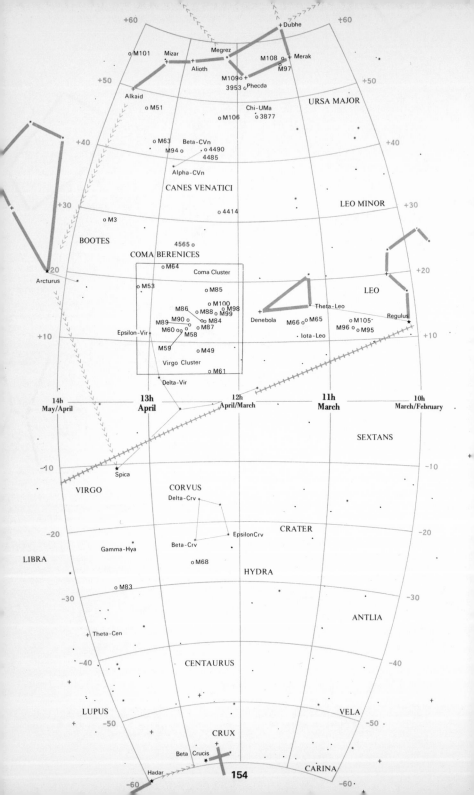

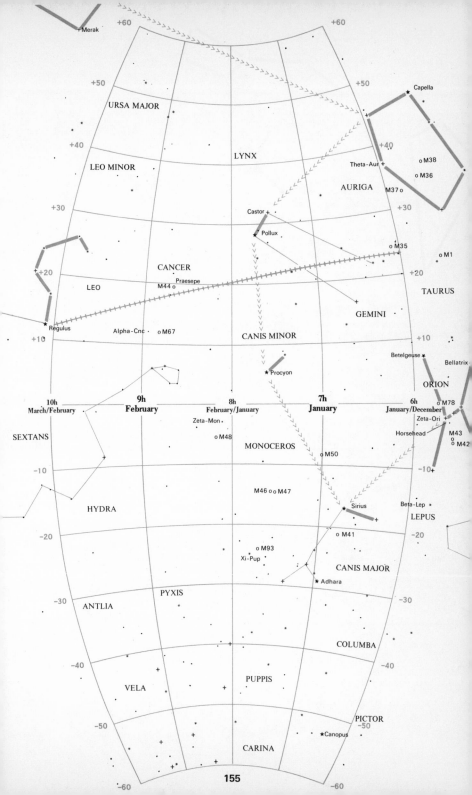

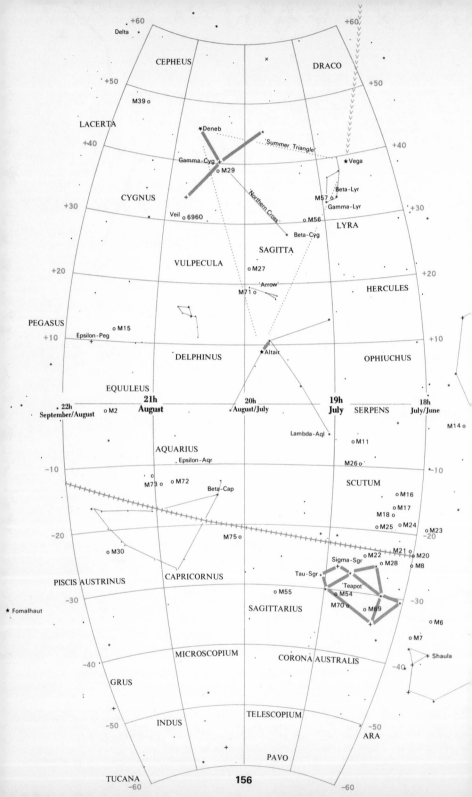

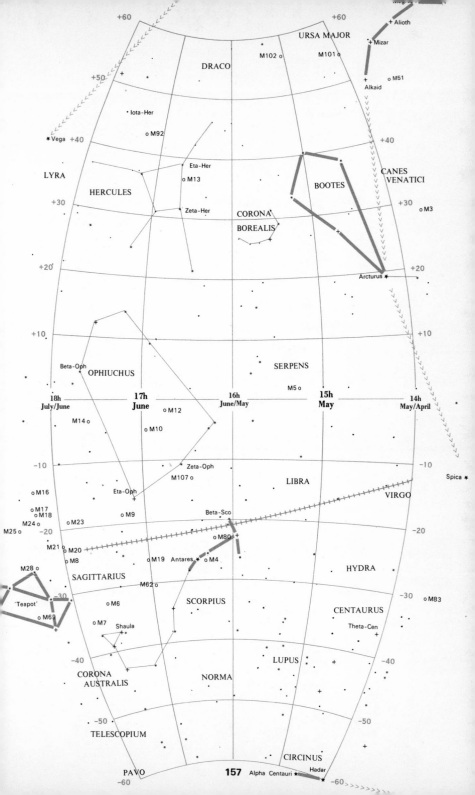

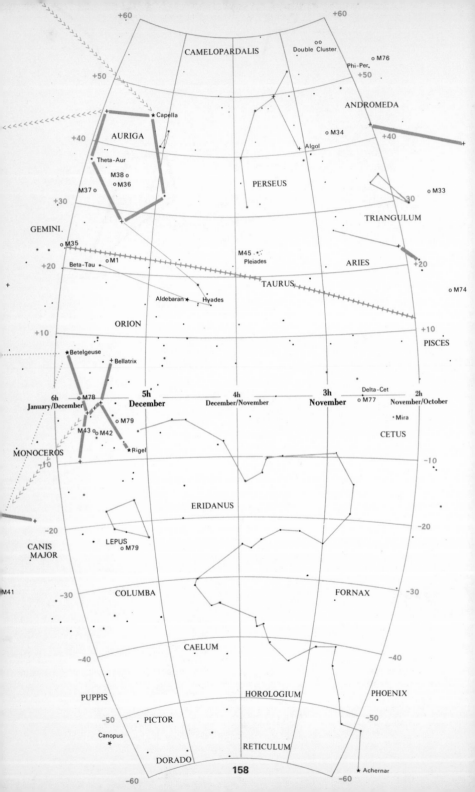

CAMELOPARDALIS

Double Cluster

o M76

Phi-Per.

+60   +60
+50   +50

ANDROMEDA

Capella

+40   o M34

AURIGA

Theta-Aur   Algol

PERSEUS   o M33

M38 o
o M36

M37 o   30

+30   TRIANGULUM

GEMINI.   ARIES

o M35

M45   Pleiades   +20   +20

Beta-Tau   o M1

TAURUS   o M74

Aldebaran   Hyades

ORION   +10   +10

PISCES

Betelgeuse

Bellatrix

Delta-Cet

6h   5h   4h   3h   o M77   2h
o M78

January/December   December   December/November   November   November/October

Mira

M43 o o M42   o M79   CETUS

Rigel

MONOCEROS

-10   -10

ERIDANUS

CANIS   -20   -20
MAJOR

LEPUS   o M79

M41   COLUMBA   -30   FORNAX   -30

CAELUM

-40   -40

PUPPIS   HOROLOGIUM   PHOENIX

-50   PICTOR   -50

Canopus

RETICULUM

DORADO   158

Achernar

-60   -60

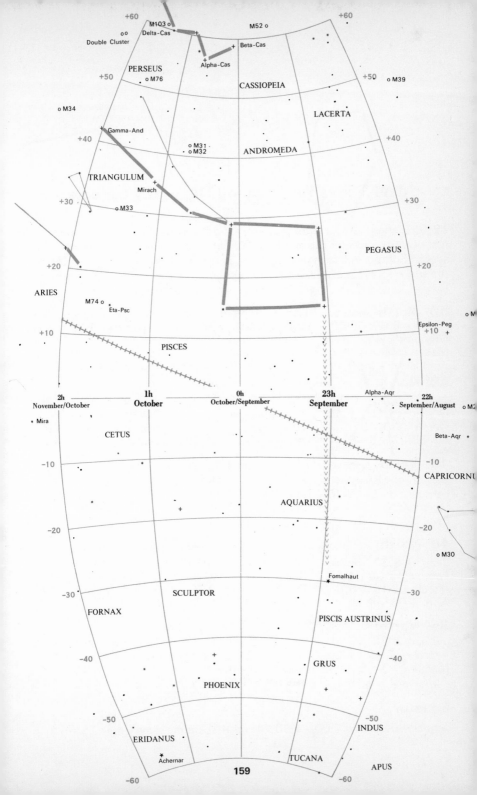

Ideal Times for Viewing Deep Sky Objects

All times shown are for *Standard Time.* Add one hour for Daylight Time. The first number indicates the end of twilight at the beginning of the month. The second number indicates the beginning of twilight in the morning, just before the sunrise. Marginal means that the sun will be still glowing on the northern horizon, but southern objects should be visible around midnight.

55° North: Moscow, Glasgow, Edmonton, South Alaska

January 6:00 - 6:00	May 10:30 - 1:30	September 9:30 - 2:30
February 6:45 - 5:45	June marginal	October 8:00 - 3:45
March 7:45 - 4:45	July marginal	November 6:45 - 4:45
April 8:45 - 3:30	August 11:15 - 1:00	December 6:00 - 5:30

50° North: Paris, London, St. John's, Winnipeg, Vancouver

January 6:15 - 6:00	May 9:45 - 2:15	September 9:00 - 3:00
February 6:45 - 5:45	June marginal	October 7:45 - 4:00
March 7:30 - 5:00	July marginal	November 6:45 - 4:45
April 8:30 - 3:45	August 10:30 - 1:30	December 6:00 - 5:30

45° North: Geneve, Halifax, Montreal, Minneapolis, Portland

January 6:15 - 5:45	May 9:00 - 2:45	September 8:30 - 3:30
February 6:45 - 5:30	June 10:00 - 1:45	October 7:30 - 4:00
March 7:30 - 5:00	July 10:30 - 1:45	November 6:45 - 4:45
April 8:15 - 4:00	August 9:45 - 2:30	December 6:15 - 5:15

40° North: Rome, Madrid, New York, Denver, San Francisco

January 6:30 - 5:30	May 8:30 - 3:15	September 8:15 - 3:45
February 7:00 - 5:30	June 9:30 - 2:30	October 7:30 - 4:15
March 7:30 - 5:00	July 9:45 - 2:30	November 6:45 - 4:45
April 8:00 - 4:15	August 9:15 - 3:00	December 6:15 - 5:15

35° North: Tel Aviv, Gibraltar, Atlanta, Los Angeles

January 6:30 - 5:30	May 8:15 - 3:30	September 8:00 - 4:00
February 7:30 - 5:30	June 9:00 - 3:00	October 7:15 - 4:15
March 7:30 - 5:00	July 9:15 - 3:00	November 6:45 - 4:45
April 8:00 - 4:15	August 8:45 - 3:15	December 6:30 - 5:15

Equator

January-December 7:00 - 4:30 All nights about the same length